INSTITUTE OF GEOLOGICAL SCIENCES

Natural Environment Research Council

Mineral Assessment Report 64

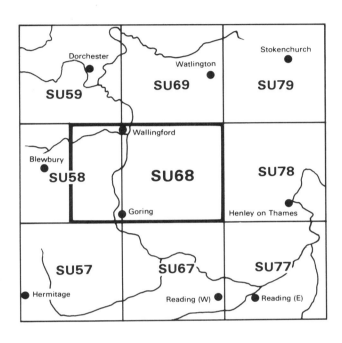

The sand and gravel resources of the country between Wallingford and Goring, Oxfordshire

Description of 1 : 25 000 sheet SU 68 and part of sheet SU 58

C.E. Corser

London   Her Majesty's Stationery Office   1981

The first twelve reports on the assessment of British sand and gravel resources appeared in the Report series of the Institute of Geological Sciences as a subseries. Report 13 and subsequent reports appear as Mineral Assessment Reports of the Institute.

Details of published reports appear at the end of this Report.

Any enquiries concerning this report may be addressed to Head, Industrial Minerals Assessment Unit, Institute of Geological Sciences, Keyworth, Nottingham NG12 5GG.

The asterisk on the cover indicates that parts of sheets adjacent to the one cited are described in this report.

PREFACE

National resources of many industrial minerals may seem so large that stocktaking appears unnecessary, but the demand for minerals and for land for all purposes is intensifying and it has become increasingly clear in recent years that regional assessments of the resources of these minerals should be undertaken. The publication of information about the quantity and quality of deposits over large areas is intended to provide a comprehensive factual background against which planning decisions can be made.

Sand and gravel, considered together as naturally occurring aggregate, was selected as the bulk mineral demanding the most urgent attention, initially in the south-east of England, where about half the national output is won and very few sources of alternative aggregates are available. Following a short feasibility project, initiated in 1966 by the Ministry of Land and Natural Resources, the Industrial Minerals Assessment Unit (formerly the Mineral Assessment Unit) of the Institute of Geological Sciences began systematic surveys in 1968. The work is now being financed by the Department of the Environment and is being undertaken with the co-operation of the Sand and Gravel Association of Great Britain.

This report describes the resources of sand and gravel of 150 km² of the country in the Thames Valley between Wallingford and Goring, shown on the accompanying 1:25 000 resource map SU 68 and part of SU 58. The survey was conducted in 1971–76 by H. C. Squirrell, C. E. Corser, P. Robson and P. G. Hoare.

The work is based on a geological survey at 1:10 560 in 1885–91 by A. J. Jukes-Brown, F. J. Bennett and J. H. Blake. The Chalk boundaries were amended by S. C. A. Holmes in 1946. The area was resurveyed by D. Foster and A. W. Kemp in 1974–76 and A. Horton amended the Chalk-Greensand boundary in 1977. J. W. Gardner, CBE (Land Agent), was responsible for negotiating access to land for drilling. The ready cooperation of land owners, tenants and gravel companies in this work is gratefully acknowledged.

G. M. Brown
Director

Institute of Geological Sciences
Exhibition Road
London SW7 2DE

January 1980

CONTENTS

The sand and gravel resources of the country between Wallingford and Goring, Oxfordshire

Description of 1:25 000 Sheet SU 68 and part of Sheet SU 58

C. E. CORSER

SUMMARY

The assessment of the sand and gravel resources in the Wallingford-Goring area, Oxfordshire, is based on the geological maps and borehole records of the Institute of Geological Sciences, records made available by the sand and gravel industry, recent field mapping and 56 boreholes drilled for the Industrial Minerals Assessment Unit.

All deposits in the area that might be potentially workable for sand and gravel have been investigated and a simple statistical method has been used to estimate the volume. The reliability of the volume estimates is given at the symmetrical 95 per cent probability level.

The 1:25 000 map is divided into four resource blocks containing between 6.2 and 14.4 km² of potentially workable sand and gravel. For each block the geology of the deposits is described and the mineral-bearing area, the mean thicknesses of overburden and mineral and the mean gradings are stated. Detailed borehole data are given. The geology, the position of the boreholes and the outlines of the resource blocks are shown on the accompanying map.

Note
National grid references are given in square brackets. All fall within the 100-km square SU, as do all borehole registration numbers.

Bibliographical reference
CORSER, C. E. 1981. The sand and gravel resources of the country between Wallingford and Goring, Oxfordshire. Description of 1:25 000 sheet SU 68 and part of sheet SU 58. *Miner. Assess. Rep. Inst. Geol. Sci.*, No. 64.

Author
C. E. Corser, BSc, BA
Institute of Geological Sciences
Keyworth, Nottingham NG12 5GG

INTRODUCTION

The survey is concerned with the estimation of resources, which include deposits that are not currently exploitable but have a foreseeable use, rather than reserves, which can only be assessed in the light of current, locally prevailing, economic considerations. Clearly, both the economic and the social factors used to decide whether a deposit may be workable in the future cannot be predicted; they are likely to change with time. Deposits not currently economically workable may be exploited as demand increases, as higher grade or alternative materials become scarce, or as improved processing techniques are applied to them. The improved knowledge of the main physical properties of the resource and their variability which this survey seeks to provide, will add significantly to the factual background against which planning policies can be decided (Archer, 1969; Thurrell, 1971; Harris and others, 1974).

The survey provides information at the 'indicated' level 'for which tonnage and grade are computed partly from specific measurements, samples or production data and partly from projection for a reasonable distance on geologic evidence. The sites available for inspection, measurement, and sampling are too widely or otherwise inappropriately spaced to permit the mineral bodies to be outlined completely or the grade established throughout' (Bureau of Mines and Geological Survey, 1948, p.15).

It follows that the whereabouts of reserves must still be established and their size and quality proved by the customary detailed exploration and evaluation undertaken by the industry. However, the information provided by this survey should assist in the selection of the best targets for such further work. The following arbitrary physical criteria have been adopted:

a The deposit should average at least 1 m in thickness.
b The ratio of overburden to sand and gravel should be no more than 3:1.
c The proportion of fines (particles passing the No. 240 mesh B.S. sieve, about $\frac{1}{16}$ mm) should not exceed 40 per cent.
d The deposit must lie within 25 m of the surface, this being taken as the likely maximum working depth under most circumstances. It follows from the second criterion that boreholes are drilled no deeper than 18 m if no sand and gravel has been proved.

A deposit of sand and gravel which broadly meets these criteria, is regarded as 'potentially workable' and is described and assessed as 'mineral' in this report. As the assessment is at the indicated level, parts of such a deposit may not satisfy all the criteria.

For the particular needs of assessing sand and gravel resources, a grain-size classification based on the geometric scale $\frac{1}{16}$ mm, $\frac{1}{4}$ mm, 1 mm, 4 mm, 16 mm has been adopted. The boundaries between fines (that is, the clay

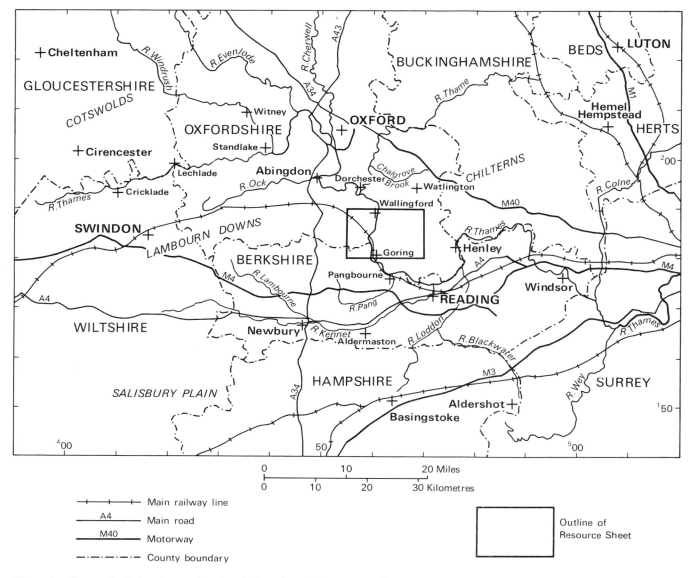

```
0        10        20 Miles
├────┬────┼────┬────┤
0   10   20      30 Kilometres
```

——+——+—— Main railway line	
—A4— Main road	
—M40— Motorway	
—·—·—·— County boundary	

Outline of Resource Sheet

Figure 1 Generalised sketch map showing the location of the resource sheet area

and silt fractions) and sand, and between sand and gravel material, are placed at $\frac{1}{16}$ mm and 4 mm respectively (see Appendix C).

The volume and other characteristics are assessed within resource blocks, each of which, ideally, contains approximately 10 km² of sand and gravel. No account is taken of any factors, for example, roads, villages and high agricultural or landscape value, which might stand in the way of sand and gravel being exploited, although towns are excluded. The estimated total volume therefore bears no simple relationship to the amount that could be extracted in practice.

It must be emphasised that the assessment applies to the resource block as a whole. Valid conclusions cannot be drawn about the mineral in parts of a block, except in the immediate vicinity of the actual sample points.

DESCRIPTION OF THE DISTRICT

This district, covering 150 km² of Oxfordshire and Berkshire, lies in the mid-Thames Valley between Wallingford and Goring (Figure 1). Wallingford, the largest town, is located in the north, about 45 miles from London and 13 miles from both Oxford and Reading.

The region is essentially agricultural but large areas of the Chiltern escarpment are covered with deciduous woodland. Recent housing developments have extended the residential areas of Wallingford, Cholsey and Goring.

TOPOGRAPHY

The district is dominated by the River Thames, which flows north–south from Wallingford to Goring (Figure 1), where it cuts through the chalk ridge of the Chiltern Hills. A wide plain formed by the Lower Chalk and Upper Greensand occupies the low-lying regions at levels between 42 and 52 m above Ordnance Datum. Remnants of former meanders enclose low rounded hills, e.g. Cholsey Hill [575 880], Mackney [577 895] and White Hill [609 845].

Elsewhere the area consists of chalk hills and coombes; the prominent ridge of the Chiltern Hills, trending NE–SW, changes direction at the Goring Gap and strikes E–W to form the Berkshire Downs to the west.

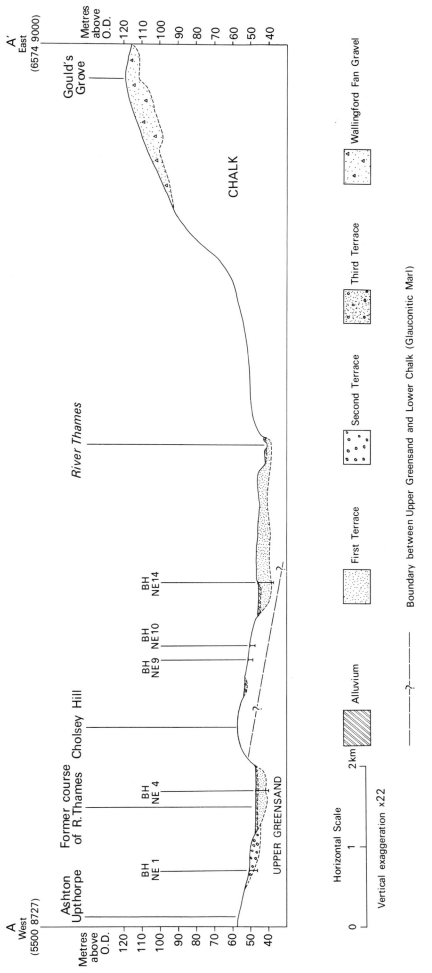

Figure 2 Generalised section across the Thames Valley between Ashton Upthorpe and Goulds Grove. (The line of section is marked on the resource sheet.)

3

Table 1 Geological succession

DRIFT	Type of deposit
RECENT AND PLEISTOCENE	
Alluvium	Recent and modern river deposits
River Terrace Deposits	River terrace deposits of the Thames
First (Floodplain or Northmoor) Terrace	
Second (Summertown -Radley) Terrace	
Third (Wolvercote Terrace)	
Fourth (Hanborough) Terrace	
Fifth Terrace	
Sixth Terrace	
Seventh Terrace	
Eighth Terrace	
Sand and gravel of unknown origin	Possibly glacial deposits
Head	Solifluction deposits of local derivation developed under periglacial conditions
Younger Coombe Deposits	
Wallingford Fan Gravel	
Clay-with-flints	Deposits possibly produced over a long period of time from the decomposition of Chalk and Eocene rocks
SOLID	
EOCENE	
Reading Beds	Fluviatile and deltaic deposits
UPPER CRETACEOUS	
Upper Chalk, including Chalk Rock	Marine deposits
Middle Chalk, including Melbourn Rock	
Lower Chalk, including Totternhoe Stone and Glauconitic Marl	
Upper Greensand	Shallow-water marine deposits

GEOLOGY

The solid rocks of the area range in age from Upper Cretaceous to Lower Eocene and dip gently (between $2°$ and $5°$) towards the south-east. Drift deposits occur as continuous spreads in the valleys, but as patches in the upland areas. Hill crests occurring between 107 and 183 m above Ordnance Datum carry deposits mainly of Clay-with-flints, with Eighth–Fifth river terraces and sand and gravel of unknown origin locally. Between 76 and 107 m above Ordnance Datum, a Middle Chalk platform is overlain by patches of Wallingford Fan Gravel. Fourth to First terraces and Alluvium occur only at elevations up to about +65 m Ordnance Datum. The geological succession of the solid and drift deposits is outlined in Table 1, and the relationship between the drift deposits is shown in Figure 2. An account of the geology was published by the Geological Survey describing the 1 in to 1 mile Geological Sheet 254 (Henley-on-Thames) (Jukes-Brown and Osborne White, 1908).

SOLID

Upper Greensand: Cropping out mainly in the north of the district, the Upper Greensand has a maximum recorded thickness of 29.9 m in I.G.S. borehole 68 SE 16, but the base was not reached; Jukes-Brown and Osborne White (1908) estimated the total thickness in the district to be between 50 and 80 m. The sequence consists of banded pale grey to pale green, fine-grained micaceous glauconitic siltstone, calcareous siltstone and sandy limestone. Locally the beds contain occasional sponges, shell fragments and pyritised burrows.

Lower Chalk: The Lower Chalk crops out intermittently along the Thames Valley, where it consists mainly of soft grey marly chalk with hard silty seams. The basal 2 to 4 m, which are commonly glauconitic and sandy, are termed the Glauconitic Marl. The Totternhoe Stone, occurring near the top of the formation, is a thin bed of hard grey chalk with brown phosphatic nodules.

Middle Chalk: This formation, cropping out on the middle and high ground of the area, consists of hard, nodular yellowish white chalk, the Melbourn Rock, at the base, passing up into firm homogeneous white chalk with beds containing nodular and tabular flints towards the top.

Upper Chalk: This formation consists of beds of white chalk with scattered nodular and tabular flints. The base of the formation is marked by a hard glauconitic and phosphatic bed (Chalk Rock) about one metre thick.

Reading Beds: Along the crest of the Chiltern Hills, the Reading Beds occur in six small outliers. Unconformably overlying the Chalk, they consist of variably coloured clays and current-bedded sands with scattered rounded pebbles, which locally form lenses, particularly near the base.

DRIFT

Clay-with-flints: This deposit extends over about 27 km^2 of country along the summits of the Chiltern ridges and as scattered patches on the Berkshire Downs. The deposit ranges in recorded thickness from 0.7 to 7.4 m and consists of unstratified yellowish red to reddish brown clay and loamy clay containing coarse (>16 mm) flints. Minor components are rounded pebbles of quartz, quartzite and concretionary ironstone. Sporadically, pockets of sandy material occur, composed of flint and quartz.

Clay-with-flints is probably a residual deposit possibly resulting from the decomposition of the Chalk and Eocene sediments.

Wallingford Fan Gravel: This deposit occurs in discrete patches along the lower slopes of the Chiltern Hills between Oakley Wood [645 888] in the north and Grove Farm [615 827] in the south. They form plateau-like features up to 1 km wide on ridge crests ranging in height from 70 to 110 m above Ordnance Datum. Individual patches are separated by steep-sided dry chalk valleys (coombes). The deposits consist mainly of clayey gravels with subordinate clay beds and are of variable thickness, a maximum of 7.7 m being recorded in borehole 68 NW 19. The deposits are probably derived from the chalk escarpment by solifluction processes. The junction between these deposits and the underlying chalk is characteristically irregular.

Younger Coombe Deposits: These deposits occur in two isolated patches in the east of the resource sheet area with a total area of 0.8 km^2. They consist of unstratified reddish brown sandy clay with poorly sorted flint gravel and fragments of chalk. These deposits are the product of solifluction processes.

4

Table 2 Mean composition of the gravel fraction of the mineral deposits

	First Terrace		Second Terrace		Third Terrace		Fifth Terrace		Wallingford Fan Gravel		Sixth to Eighth Terraces		Sand and gravel of unknown origin	
Average elevation of the base of the deposit above OD	41.5 m		48.7 m		56.5 m		90.0 m		95.3 m		120.9 m		152.0 m	
Grading size Fine (+4 −16 mm) Coarse (+16 mm)	Mean % Wt* (94)†		Mean % Wt (11)		Mean % Wt (6)		% Wt (1)		Mean % Wt (15)		Mean % Wt (23)		Mean % Wt (7)	
	Fine	Coarse	Fine	Coarse	Fine	Coarse	Fine	Coarse	Fine	Coarse	Fine	Coarse	Fine	Coarse
Flint	25	69	18	54	41	85	52	41	86	98	55	87	57	92
Quartz and quartzite (including Bunter Sandstone)	4	9	11	37	7	5	45	45	5	1	33	11	39	2
Limestone and chalk	60	21	60	8	48	9	tr	0	1	tr	4	2	1	1
Ironstone	10	tr	11	tr	4	1	3	14	7	0	6	0	2	0
Minor constituents	1	1	0	1	tr	tr	0	0	1	tr	2	tr	1	5

*The percentage shown is the arithmetic mean of weighted means of samples from individual boreholes

†The figure shown in brackets is the number of samples used in the calculation

Head: These solifluction deposits, derived mainly from Cretaceous rocks, are scattered widely in the bottoms of dry valleys or fringe other drift deposits adjacent to steep slopes. The deposits range in thickness from 1 to 3 m and consist of structureless silty, sandy and chalky clay, with sporadic seams of sand with scattered flint and quartzite pebbles.

Sand and gravel of unknown origin: Small scattered patches of this deposit cap the crests of the Chilterns and the Berkshire Downs. In the south-east of the area the largest of the deposits are found at Woodcote [645 821], Checkendon [664 830] and Witheridge Hill [696 843]. On the Berkshire Downs, two patches are located at Unhill Wood [562 823] and Common Wood [582 804]. The deposits were proved in IMAU boreholes to be up to 6.1 m thick and consist of flint, quartz and quartzite pebbles enclosed in a reddish brown sandy clay matrix. Traces of ironstone, chert and chalk are sometimes present. These deposits are thought (Hey, 1965) to result from glacial outwash, being derived mainly from the 'Bunter' Pebble Beds of the Midlands. Alternatively a marine origin has been postulated (Wooldridge, 1939).

River Terrace Deposits: The *Eighth to Fifth terraces* cover an area of 7.7 km² on the Chilterns and on the Berkshire Downs. The deposits, which range in recorded thickness from 0.6 m to 7.0 m, consist of ill-sorted mixtures of clay, sand and gravel. In a trench exposure [58 SE 26] north-west of Moulsford, Fifth Terrace deposits consist of fine to cobble-size gravel in a brown 'very clayey' sand matrix, without bedding being apparent.

Two small remnants of the *Fourth (Hanborough) Terrace* cap rounded hillocks north-west of Moulsford [587 844] and North Moreton [500 820]. The deposit consists of pebbles of sandy limestone and flint with occasional lenses of silt or silty clay.

Remnants of the *Third (Wolvercote) Terrace* cover 0.4 km² on the eastern and western flanks of the Thames Valley. At South Stoke [605 841] the deposit consists of 8.3 m of 'very clayey' sand with flint and chalk pebbles (borehole 68 SW 9).

The *Second (Summertown–Radley) Terrace* covers 3.8 km² on the western flank of the Thames Valley. The largest patch of the deposit occupies a former course of the River Thames north of Cholsey lying between 51.8 and 56.4 m above Ordnance Datum. The deposits here comprise 'clayey' sandy gravel up to 3.0 m thick containing limestone and flint with some quartz, quartzite, chalk and ironstone pebbles.

The *First (Floodplain or Northmoor) Terrace* extends continuously over 24.6 km², but about half is overlain by Alluvium. A maximum thickness of 6.2 m of sandy gravel has been proved in IMAU borehole 58 NE 14. The deposits occurring along the former course of the River Thames near Cholsey [588 863] are about 2 m thicker than those in the present-day valley. The deposits consist of well-sorted, well-stratified and cross-bedded sands with pebbles of flint and Jurassic limestone and minor amounts of ironstone, chalk, quartz and quartzite.

The First Terrace Deposits are a major potential source of sand and gravel in the district although they have not been commercially exploited to date.

Alluvium: This deposit, which is up to 3.4 m thick, is present over an area of 12.6 km² of the Thames Valley reaching its greatest extent along the former course of the River Thames west of Cholsey. It consists of dark grey calcareous loams, silts and clays with sporadic lenses of sand and fine gravel, seams of peat and Recent molluscan shells.

WALLINGFORD FAN GRAVEL

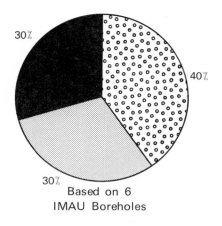

30%

40%

30%

Based on 6
IMAU Boreholes

SAND AND GRAVEL OF UNKNOWN AGE

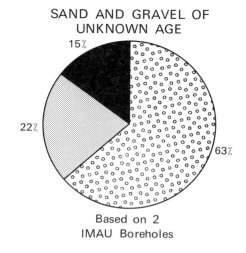

15%

22%

63%

Based on 2
IMAU Boreholes

EIGHTH TO FIFTH TERRACES

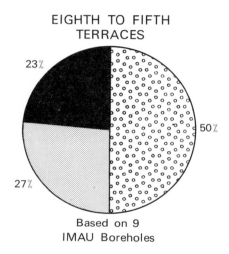

23%

27%

50%

Based on 9
IMAU Boreholes

FOURTH TO FIRST TERRACES

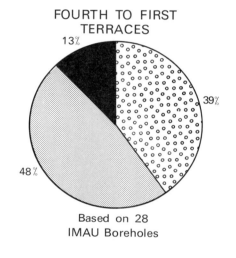

13%

48%

39%

Based on 28
IMAU Boreholes

 Gravel   Sand   Fines

Figure 3   Mean grading of the aggregate-bearing deposits.

COMPOSITION OF THE SAND AND GRAVEL

On the basis of lithology and topographic level the potentially workable sand and gravel deposits of the area may be grouped as follows: Eighth to Fifth terraces; Fourth to First terraces; Wallingford Fan Gravel; and sand and gravel of unknown origin. The mean grading of these deposits is shown in Figure 3. Additionally, the mean composition of the fine gravel fraction of all but the Fourth Terrace deposits is shown in Figure 4. The mean compositions of the fine and coarse gravel fraction in potentially workable deposits are compared in Table 2. Local variations in composition and grade of the mineral proved in IMAU boreholes are shown in Figures 5 and 6 respectively. Gross variations in grade of the potentially workable deposits are shown in Figure 7.

Eighth to Fifth terraces: Overall, these deposits comprise 'very clayey' gravel (Figure 3). The gravel is predominantly subangular to subrounded flint with well-rounded quartz and quartzite and minor proportions of ironstone, chalk and other constituents; coarse gravel fractions contain a higher proportion of flint.   Sand is mainly composed of quartz and flint grains with varying amounts of chalk. The fines comprise brown to grey silts and clays, sometimes with black manganese staining. Locally the composition of the deposits is influenced by the underlying bedrock. For example, where they overlie the Glauconitic Marl (Lower Chalk) the basal part of the deposits is frequently glauconitic and contains subordinate amounts of greyish green marly siltstone and chalk.

6

WALLINGFORD FAN GRAVEL

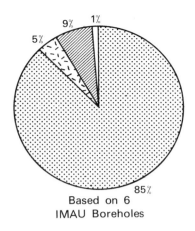

9% 1%
5%

85%

Based on 6
IMAU Boreholes

SAND AND GRAVEL OF
UNKNOWN AGE

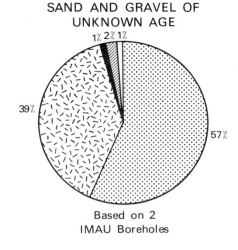

1% 2% 1%

39%

57%

Based on 2
IMAU Boreholes

EIGHTH TO FIFTH
TERRACES

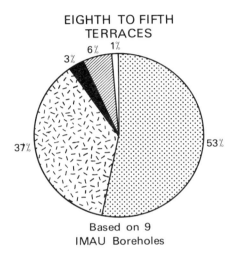

6% 1%
3%

37%

53%

Based on 9
IMAU Boreholes

THIRD TERRACE

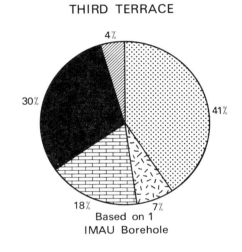

4%

30%

41%

18%   7%

Based on 1
IMAU Borehole

SECOND TERRACE

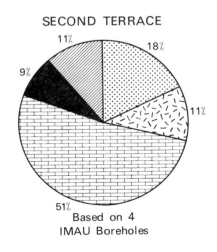

11%   18%

9%

11%

51%

Based on 4
IMAU Boreholes

FIRST TERRACE

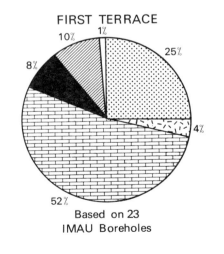

10%   1%

8%   25%

4%

52%

Based on 23
IMAU Boreholes

 Flint　　 Quartz and Quartzite　　 Limestone　　 Chalk　　 Ironstone　　☐ Minor Constituents

Figure 4　Mean composition of the fine gravel (+4−16 mm) fraction.

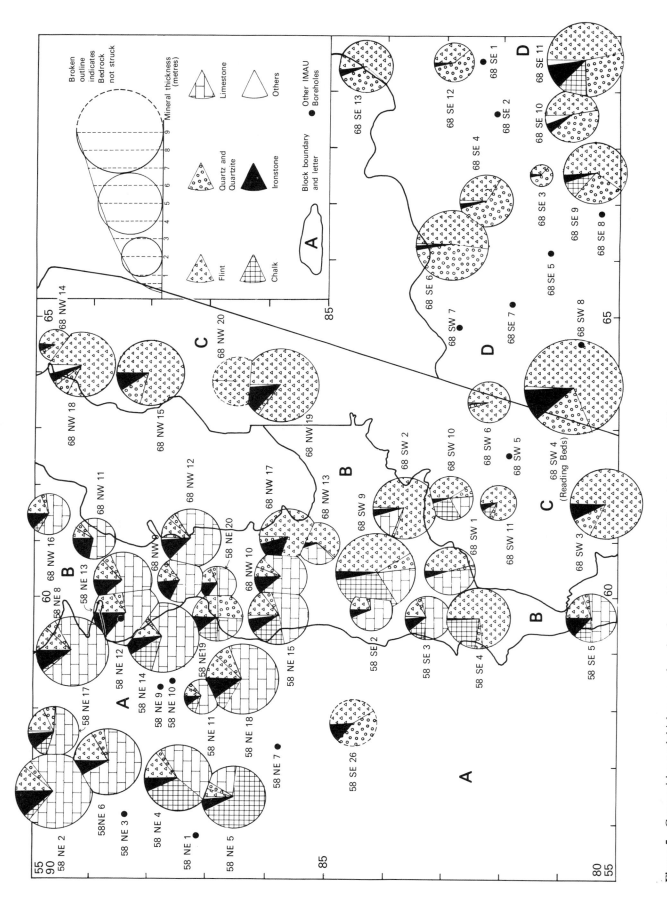

Figure 5 Composition and thicknesses of sand and gravel in Industrial Minerals Assessment Unit boreholes.

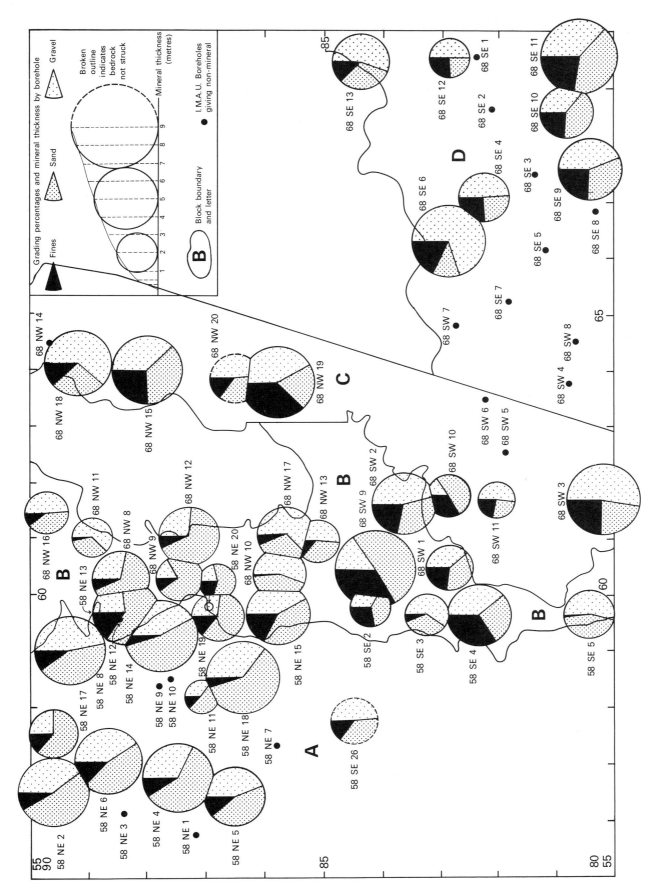

Figure 6 Grading characteristics and thicknesses of sand and gravel in Industrial Minerals Assessment Unit boreholes.

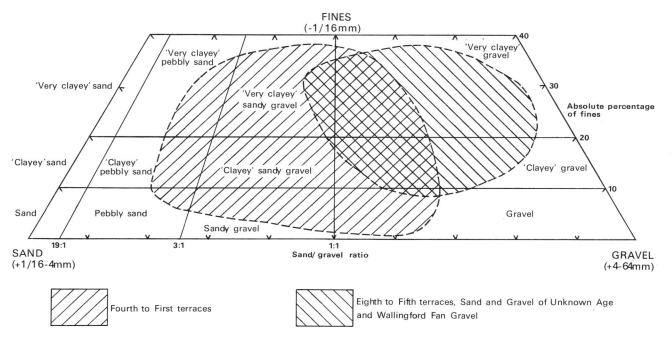

Figure 7 Diagram showing the range in grading of the potentially workable drift deposits.

Fourth to First terraces: These deposits are principally 'clayey' sandy gravels although the Third and Fourth terraces may vary in grade.

In the First and Second terraces the fine gravel fractions contain subrounded limestone with subangular flint and minor amounts of ironstone, chalk, quartz and quartzite. In the Third Terrace, fine gravel is predominantly of flint and chalk with a little limestone, quartz and quartzite. The coarse fractions are composed of well-rounded flint and quartz, which are concentrated at the base of the deposits. The sand is mainly brown to greyish white quartz and flint locally with some chalk or glauconite. The fines content, which increases with increasing age of the terraces, is composed of grey silt and clay.

Wallingford Fan Gravel: These deposits commonly grade as 'very clayey' gravel. The gravel comprises predominantly coarse and cobble-size flint; however, the fine gravel fraction, in addition to flint, contains some chalk, quartz and minor constituents. The sand comprises quartz and flint grains with some chalk. A brown clayey matrix accounts for the high fines content.

Sand and gravel of unknown origin: These deposits usually consist of 'very clayey' gravel. The gravel fraction consists of fine subangular to subrounded flint with subordinate well- rounded brown to reddish brown quartz, quartzite and sandstone pebbles possibly derived from the 'Bunter' Pebble Beds of the Midlands. Coarse gravels (composed of subangular flint) are present within the basal 0.5 m of the deposit, with minor constituents of ironstone and chalk. The sand comprises lithic grains similar to those present in the gravels. The fines occur as a yellow or reddish brown clayey matrix.

THE MAP
The sand and gravel resource map is folded into the pocket at the end of this report. The base map is the Ordnance Survey 1:25 000 Outline Edition in grey, on which the topography is shown by contours in green, the

geological data in black and the mineral resource information in shades of red.

Geological data: The geological boundary lines and symbols shown are taken from the recently surveyed six-inch sheets which form part of the published Henley-on-Thames (254) 1:50 000 geological map of the Institute's Field Staff; the mapping was supplemented by borehole and pit section data collected during the assessment survey. Although the geological boundaries are the best interpretation of the information available at the time of survey, it is possible that local irregularities or discrepancies will be revealed by subsequent boreholes particularly where the older river terraces and sand and gravel of unknown origin overlie the Clay-with-flints.

Mineral resource information: The mineral-bearing ground is divided into resource blocks (see Appendix A). Within a resource block the mineral is subdivided into areas where it is 'exposed' and the areas where it is present in continuous (or almost continuous) spreads beneath overburden. The mineral is identified as 'exposed' where the overburden, commonly consisting only of soil and sub-soil, averages less than 1.0 m in thickness. Beneath overburden the mineral may be continuous, almost continuous or discontinuous. As potentially workable sand and gravel was proved in 85 per cent of the boreholes drilled through overburden on the present sheet area, the mineral is regarded as continuous or almost continuous.

Areas where bedrock crops out, and where sand and gravel does not satisfy the definition of mineral, are uncoloured on the map. In such areas it has been assumed that mineral is absent except in infrequent and relatively minor patches, which can neither be outlined nor assessed quantitatively in the context of this survey.

The area of the exposed sand and gravel is measured from the mapped geological boundary lines. The whole of this area is considered as mineral, although it may include small areas where sand and gravel is not present or is not potentially workable.

Table 3 Statistical assessment of sand and gravel resources: blocks A to D

Resource block	Area (km²)						Mean thickness(m)		Volume of mineral			Mean grading percentage		
	Block	Mineral					Over-burden	Mineral	million m³	95% confidence limits		Fines	Sand	Gravel
		Younger River Terraces (4–1)	Older River Terraces (8–5)	Walling-ford Fan Gravel	Sand and gravel of unknown origin	Total				±%	± million m³	$-\frac{1}{16}$mm	$+\frac{1}{16}-4$mm	$+4$mm
A	43.6	13.6	0.4		0.3	14.3	1.0	3.9	55.9	42	23.5	10	51	39
B	19.1	14.4				14.4	1.2	3.6	51.8	21	10.9	14	46	40
C	21.7		0.9	5.3		6.2	0.4	3.4	21.2	56	11.8	24	30	46
D	24.3		6.4		1.9	8.3	2.0	2.7	22.4	67	15.0	22	28	50
A to D	108.7	28.0	7.7	5.3	2.2	43.2	1.2	3.4	151.3	18	27.2			

RESULTS

The statistical results are summarised in Table 3 and Figure 9. Fuller grading particulars for resource blocks A, B, C and D are shown in Tables 4, 5, 6 and 7 respectively. For the four resource blocks, the accuracy of results at the 95 per cent probability level ranges from 21 to 67 per cent (that is, it is probable that 19 times out of 20 the true volume present lies within these limits). However, the true values are more likely to be nearer the figures estimated than the limits. Moreover, it is probable that in each block approximately the same percentage limits would apply for the estimate of volume of a very much smaller parcel of ground (say 100 hectares) containing similar sand and gravel deposits, if the results from the same number of sample points (as provided by, say, ten boreholes) were used in the calculation. Thus, if closer limits are needed for the quotation of the reserves in part of a block, it can be expected that data from more than ten sample points will be required, even if the area is quite small. This point can be illustrated by considering the whole of the potentially workable sand and gravel on this sheet. The total volume (151.3 million m³) can be estimated to limits of ±18 per cent at the 95 per cent probability level, by a calculation based on the data from 211 sample points spread across the four resource blocks. However, it must be emphasised that the quoted volume of sand and gravel has no simple relationship with the amount that could be extracted in practice, since no allowance has been made in the calculations for any restraints (such as existing buildings and roads) on the use of land for mineral working.

NOTES ON RESOURCE BLOCKS

The resource block boundaries are drawn to encompass areas of sand and gravel of similar stratigraphy and lithology and to reflect the distribution of the potentially workable sand and gravel deposits (Figure 8).

Block A

This block of 43.6 km² occupies the entire western part of the area, and contains 14.3 km² of mineral, which overlies Lower Chalk in the south and Upper Greensand in the north. About 95 per cent of the mineral (13.6 km²) lies along the former course of the River Thames between Cholsey [588 863] and Mackney [580 900] in the northern part of the block, where it consists of First, Second and Third terrace deposits. The remaining 0.7 km² of mineral, comprising Fourth and Fifth terraces and sand and gravel of unknown origin, forms small scattered patches on the foothills of the Berkshire Downs in the south of the block.

The assessment of resources is based on 12 IMAU boreholes (Table 4) and 18 other records. A maximum thickness of 6.2 m of mineral has been recorded in IMAU borehole 58 NE 14; the mean thickness for the block is 3.9 m. The estimated volume of mineral is 55.9 m³ ±42 per cent. The mean grading of the block is fines 10 per cent, sand 51 per cent and gravel 39 per cent.

The fines content ranges from 5 per cent in boreholes 58 NE 14 and NE 18 to 15 per cent in trench section 58 SE 26. The sand content ranges from 36 per cent in trench section 58 SE 26 to 61 per cent in borehole 58 NE 17 and consists of medium to coarse grades of limestone, quartz and flint with minor amounts of ironstone and glauconite. The gravel content ranges from 25 per cent in borehole 58 NE 17 to 49 per cent in trench section 58 SE 26 and consists predominantly of fine to coarse sub-rounded pebbles of limestone and chalk. The overburden ranges in thickness from 0.1 m in borehole 58 SE 26 to 2.8 m in borehole 58 NE 18 and the mean is 1.0 m. Waste bands (1.8 and 1.0 m thick) are present within the mineral in boreholes 58 NE 4 and 6 respectively.

Block B

This block extends over 19.1 km² of the Thames Valley from the Goring Gap [597 802], which is at a height of 43 m above Ordnance Datum northwards for 10 km to Wallingford [613 898] at a height of about 46 m above Ordnance Datum. The mineral of this block comprises mainly First Terrace Deposits, which occur as a continuous narrow outcrop which flanks the River Thames.

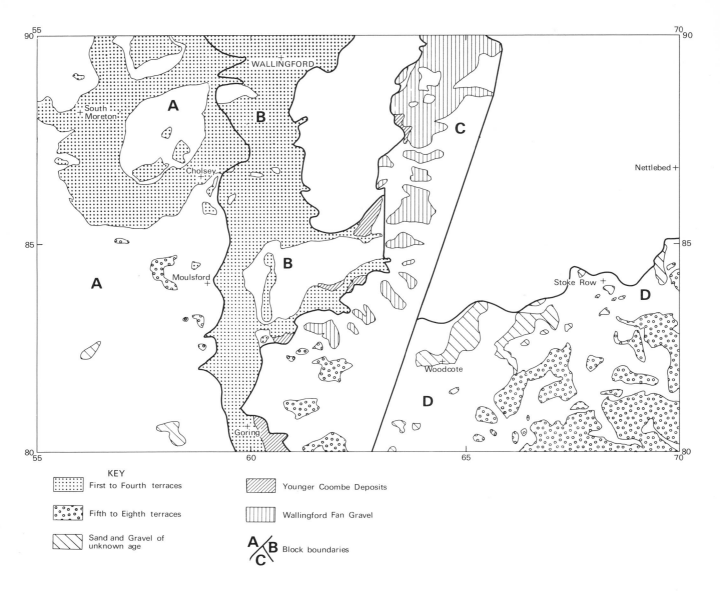

KEY

First to Fourth terraces

Fifth to Eighth terraces

Sand and Gravel of unknown age

Younger Coombe Deposits

Wallingford Fan Gravel

A/B/C Block boundaries

Figure 8 Map showing resource block boundaries in relation to potentially workable sand and gravel deposits.

Table 4 Block A: data from assessment boreholes

Borehole number*	Thickness (m)		Mean grading percentage						Mineral deposit	Lithological description (see Figure 12)
	Over-burden	Mineral	Fines	Sand			Gravel			
			$-\frac{1}{16}$mm	Fine $+\frac{1}{16}-\frac{1}{4}$mm	Medium $+\frac{1}{4}-1$mm	Coarse $+1-4$mm	Fine $+4-16$mm	Coarse $+16$mm		
58 NE 2	2.4	5.8	9	4	30	18	25	14	Alluvium/First Terrace	Sandy gravel
58 NE 3		absent							Second Terrace	
58 NE 4	0.8	5.5	9	6	34	19	25	7	Alluvium/First Terrace	Sandy gravel
58 NE 5	1.3	4.3	12	15	16	13	29	15	Alluvium/First Terrace	'Clayey' sandy gravel
58 NE 6	1.7	5.2	13	2	31	13	29	12	Alluvium/First Terrace	'Clayey' sandy gravel
58 NE 7		absent							Alluvium	
58 NE 8	1.1	5.7	10	2	21	20	25	22	Alluvium/First Terrace	'Clayey' gravel
58 NE 11	0.8	1.4	13	6	28	19	28	6	Second Terrace	'Clayey' sandy gravel
58 NE 14	0.6	6.2	5	5	23	25	34	8	First Terrace	Sandy gravel
58 NE 17	0.5	2.8	14	12	32	17	20	5	Second Terrace	'Clayey' sandy gravel
58 NE 18	2.8	5.8	5	17	25	18	29	6	First Terrace	'Clayey' sandy gravel
58 SE 26	0.1	2.4+	15	11	18	7	21	28	Fifth Terrace	'Clayey' gravel

*All fall within 100-km square SU

12

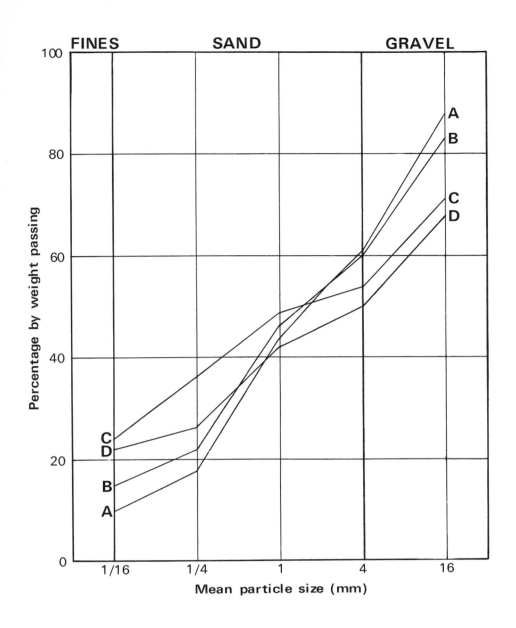

Figure 9   Mean particle-size distribution for the assessed thickness of mineral in resource blocks A to D.

Block	Percentage by weight passing				
	1/16mm	1/4mm	1mm	4mm	16mm
A	10	18	44	61	88
B	14	22	46	60	84
C	24	36	49	54	71
D	22	27	43	50	68

13

Table 5 Block B: data from assessment boreholes

Borehole number*	Thickness (m)		Mean grading percentage						Mineral deposit	Lithological description (see Figure 12)
	Over-burden	Mineral	Fines	Sand			Gravel			
				Fine	Medium	Coarse	Fine	Coarse		
			$-\frac{1}{16}$mm	$+\frac{1}{16}-\frac{1}{4}$mm	$+\frac{1}{4}-1$mm	$+1-4$mm	$+4-16$mm	$+16$mm		
58 NE 13	0.7	5.1	16	6	38	17	20	3	First Terrace	'Clayey' sandy gravel
58 NE 15	1.1	4.3	18	8	19	13	27	15	Second Terrace	'Clayey' gravel
58 NE 19	0.3	3.0	15	15	27	16	22	5	Second Terrace	'Clayey' sandy gravel
58 NE 20	0.4	1.6	21	10	25	17	21	6	Second Terrace	'V. clayey' sandy gravel
58 SE 2	1.7	2.1	28	4	28	7	25	8	First Terrace	'V. clayey' sandy gravel
58 SE 3	2.7	2.3	6	1	17	16	36	24	Alluvium/First Terrace	Gravel
58 SE 4	0.2	4.8	34	2	13	12	24	15	First Terrace	'V. clayey' gravel
58 SE 5	1.8	3.1	2	3	20	21	30	24	Alluvium/First Terrace	'V. clayey' sandy gravel
68 NW 8	1.0	4.0	7	5	44	16	20	8	First Terrace	Sandy gravel
68 NW 9	1.2	2.6	10	17	48	8	15	2	First Terrace	'Clayey' pebbly sand
68 NW 10	3.4	3.1	2	2	11	29	47	9	Alluvium/First Terrace	Gravel
68 NW 11	1.6	2.0	3	2	18	15	36	26	Alluvium/First Terrace	Sandy gravel
68 NW 12	1.4	4.3	7	9	39	19	22	4	First Terrace	Sandy gravel
68 NW 13	0.8	2.3	14	7	20	7	19	33	First Terrace	'Clayey' gravel
68 NW 16	1.7	2.1	11	8	20	12	29	20	First Terrace	'Clayey' gravel
68 NW 17	0.3	3.8	6	8	15	8	19	44	First Terrace	Gravel
68 SW 1	1.3	2.9	23	8	21	9	18	21	First Terrace	'V. clayey' gravel
68 SW 2	0.2	4.8	22	2	15	15	20	26	First Terrace	'V. clayey' gravel
68 SW 9	0.2	8.3	33	26	20	6	10	5	Third Terrace	'V. clayey' pebbly sand

*All fall within 100-km square SU

The terrace deposits are locally overlain by Alluvium. The remainder of the block consists of small patches of Second Terrace occurring at Cholsey [594 866] and at a locality [603 899] near Wallingford, together with a small area of Third Terrace flanking the Thames near South Stoke [604 840].

The assessment of resources is based on 19 IMAU boreholes (Table 5), 11 Hydrogeology Unit records and 48 other records. The mineral ranges in thickness from 1.6 m in borehole 58 NE 20 to 8.3 m in borehole 68 SW 9 with a mean of 3.6 m. The estimated volume of the mineral is 51.8 million m^3 ±21 per cent. The mean grading of the block is fines 14 per cent, sand 46 per cent and gravel 40 per cent.

The fines content ranges from 2 per cent in borehole 58 SE 5 to 34 per cent in borehole 58 SE 4. The sand fraction is mainly of medium and coarse grades ranging from 27 per cent in borehole 58 SE 4 to 73 per cent in borehole 68 NW 9. It consists of limestone, flint and quartz with minor amounts of chalk, ironstone and glauconite. The gravel content ranges from 15 per cent in borehole 68 SW 9 to 63 per cent in borehole 68 NW 17. The overburden ranges in thickness from 0.2 m in boreholes 68 SW 2, 9 and 58 SE 4 to 3.4 m in borehole 68 NW 10; the mean is 1.2 m.

Block C
This block extends along the base of the Chiltern Chalk escarpment over an area of 21.7 km² and contains all the Wallingford Fan Gravel occurring on the resource sheet (5.3 km² in area). Additionally, in the southern part of the block, six small patches of terrace deposits occupy an area of 0.9 km².

This block contains the only active sand and gravel working in the district, located in the Wallingford Fan Gravel near Oakley Wood [640 890]. Disused workings extend over about 0.36 km². All the mineral deposits in this block lie above the water table.

The assessment of resources is based on eight IMAU boreholes (Table 6), three Hydrogeology Unit records and 81 other records. The mineral ranges in thickness from 1.5 m in borehole 68 SW 11 to 6.3 m in borehole 68 SW 3, with a mean of 3.5 m. Although sand and gravel was not found in IMAU borehole 68 NW 14, this result was taken into account in the assessment of resources. The estimated volume of the mineral is 21.2 m³ ±56 per cent. The mean grading of the block is fines 24 per cent, sand 30 per cent and gravel 46 per cent.

The fines content ranges from 12 per cent in borehole 68 NW 18 to 36 per cent in borehole 68 NW 19. The sand component is mainly of medium grade quartz and flint and it ranges from 21 per cent in borehole 68 NW 19 to 39 per cent in borehole 68 SW 10. The gravel ranges from 30 per cent in borehole 68 SW 10 to 62 per cent in borehole 68 NW 18 and consists of fine to cobble-size subangular flint. Overburden is usually less than 0.4 m thick although, in borehole 68 NW 19, 3.7 m was proved. In general, mineral-bearing areas are characterised by a light sandy soil containing numerous flint pebbles.

14

Table 6 Block C: data from assessment boreholes

| Borehole number* | Thickness (m) | | Mean grading percentage | | | | | | Mineral deposit | Lithological description (see Figure 12) |
| | Over-burden | Mineral | Fines | Sand | | | Gravel | | | |
			$-\frac{1}{16}$mm	Fine $+\frac{1}{16}-\frac{1}{4}$mm	Medium $+\frac{1}{4}-1$mm	Coarse $+1-4$mm	Fine $+4-16$mm	Coarse $+16$mm		
68 NW 14		absent							Wallingford Fan Gravel	
68 NW 15	0.2	5.6	26	12	21	3	15	23	Wallingford Fan Gravel	'V. clayey' gravel
68 NW 18	0.3	5.2	12	12	10	4	25	37	Wallingford Fan Gravel	'Clayey' gravel
68 NW 19	3.7	4.3	36	9	8	4	12	31	Wallingford Fan Gravel	'V. clayey' gravel
68 NW 20	0.1	3.0+	15	20	15	1	13	36	Wallingford Fan Gravel	'Clayey' gravel
68 SW 3	0.4	6.3	25	4	11	7	25	28	Seventh Terrace	'V. clayey' sandy gravel
68 SW 10	0.1	2.2	31	19	15	5	11	19	Wallingford Fan Gravel	'V. clayey' sandy gravel
68 SW 11	0.1	1.5	22	8	9	9	18	34	Seventh Terrace	'V. clayey' gravel

*All fall within 100-km square SU

Block D

This block occupies an area of 24.3 km² of which 8.3 km² is mineral-bearing. The mineral deposits comprise Eighth to Sixth terraces and sand and gravel of unknown origin. These deposits are widely scattered and are variable in thickness, composition and grading. They overlie the Upper Chalk, Reading Beds and Clay-with-flints.

The assessment of resources is based on 11 IMAU boreholes of which four (Table 7) proved no mineral. The results of these latter boreholes have been taken into account in the assessment of the resources since the barren areas have not been delineated on the resource map.

The mineral ranges in thickness from 2.0 m in borehole 68 SE 12 to 7.0 m in borehole 68 SE 11; the mean is 2.7 m. The estimated volume of the mineral is 22.4 million m² ±67 per cent. The mean grading for the block is fines 22 per cent, sand 28 per cent and gravel 50 per cent.

The fines content ranges from 13 per cent in the trench section 58 SE 13 to 26 per cent in boreholes 68 SE 4 and 12. The sand fraction ranges from 13 per cent in borehole 68 SE 6 to 42 per cent in borehole 68 SE 11 and consists mainly of quartz and flint. The gravel, which is mainly coarser grained with occasional cobbles, ranges from 36 per cent in borehole 68 SE 11 to 68 per cent in borehole 68 SE 6; it consists of subangular flint and subrounded to rounded quartz and quartzite with minor amounts of ironstone and chalk. The overburden has a maximum thickness of 7.3 m in borehole 68 SE 4 and a mean of 2.0 m.

Table 7 Block D: data from assessment boreholes

| Borehole number* | Thickness (m) | | Mean grading percentage | | | | | | Mineral deposit | Lithological description (see Figure 12) |
| | Over-burden | Mineral | Fines | Sand | | | Gravel | | | |
			$-\frac{1}{16}$mm	Fine $+\frac{1}{16}-\frac{1}{4}$mm	Medium $+\frac{1}{4}-1$mm	Coarse $+1-4$mm	Fine $+4-16$mm	Coarse $+16$mm		
68 SW 7		absent							Sand and gravel of unknown origin	
68 SE 3		absent							Eighth Terrace	
68 SE 4	7.3	3.1	26	2	12	11	25	24	Eighth Terrace	'Very clayey' gravel
68 SE 5		absent							Eighth Terrace and Clay-with-flints	
68 SE 6	1.3	6.1	19	1	9	3	13	55	Sand and gravel of unknown origin	'Clayey' gravel
68 SE 8		absent							Seventh to Eighth Terrace	
68 SE 9	1.1	4.7	24	6	16	10	16	28	Seventh to Eighth Terrace	'Very clayey' gravel
68 SE 10	4.0	3.3	25	2	17	5	18	33	Sixth to Seventh Terrace	'Very clayey' gravel
68 SE 11	0.4	7.0	22	6	30	6	13	23	Sixth to Seventh Terrace	'Very clayey' sandy gravel
68 SE 12	0.0	2.0	26	8	9	7	19	31	Sixth to Eighth Terrace	'Very clayey' gravel
68 SE 13	0.1	3.5	13	12	10	9	32	24	Sand and gravel of unknown origin	'Clayey' gravel

*All fall within 100-km square SU

APPENDIX A

FIELD AND LABORATORY PROCEDURES

Trial and error during initial studies of the complex and variable glacial deposits of East Anglia and Essex showed that an absolute minimum of five sample points evenly distributed across the sand and gravel are needed to provide a worthwhile statistical assessment, but that, where possible, there should be not less than ten. Sample points are any points for which adequate information exists about the nature and thickness of the deposit and may include boreholes other than those drilled during the survey and exposures. In particular, the cooperation of sand and gravel operators ensures that boreholes are not drilled where reliable information is already available; although this may be used in the calculations, it is held confidentially by the Institute and cannot be disclosed.

The mineral shown on each 1:25 000 sheet is divided into resource blocks. The arbitrary size selected, 10 km², is a compromise to meet the aims of the survey by providing sufficient sample points in each block. As far as possible the block boundaries are determined by geological boundaries so that, for example, glacial and river terrace gravels are separated. Otherwise division is by arbitrary lines, which may bear no relationship to the geology. The blocks are drawn provisionally before drilling begins.

A reconnaissance of the ground is carried out to record any exposures and inquiries are made to ascertain what borehole information is available. Borehole sites are then selected to provide an even pattern of sample points at a density of approximately one per square kilometre. However, because broad trends are independently overlain by smaller scale characteristically random variations, it is unnecessary to adhere to a square grid pattern. Thus such factors as ease of access and the need to minimise disturbance to land and the public are taken into account in siting the holes; at the same time it is necessary to guard against the possibility that ease of access (that is, the positions of roads and farms) may reflect particular geological conditions, which may bias the drilling results.

The drilling machine employed should be capable of providing a continuous sample representative of all unconsolidated deposits, so that the in-situ grading can be determined, if necessary, to a depth of 30 m at a diameter of about 200 mm, beneath different types of overburden. It should be reliable, quiet, mobile and relatively small (so that it can be moved to sites of difficult access). Shell and auger rigs have proved to be almost ideal.

The rigs are modified to enable deposits above the water table to be drilled 'dry', instead of with water added to facilitate the drilling, to minimise the amount of material drawn in from outside the limits of the hole. The samples thus obtained are representative of the in-situ grading, and satisfy one of the most important aims of the survey. Below the water table the rigs are used conventionally, although this may result in the loss of some of the fines fraction and the pumping action of the bailer tends to draw unwanted material into the hole from the sides or the bottom.

A continuous series of bulk samples is taken throughout the sand and gravel. Ideally samples are composed exclusively of the whole of the material encountered in the borehole between stated depths. However, care is taken to discard, as far as possible, material which has caved or has been pumped from the bottom of the hole. A new sample is commenced whenever there is an appreciable lithological change within the sand and gravel, or at every 1 m depth. The samples, each weighing between 25 and 45 kg, are despatched in heavy duty polythene bags to a laboratory for grading. The grading procedure is based on British Standard 1377 (1967). Random checks on the accuracy of the grading are made in the Institute's laboratories.

All data, including mean grading analysis figures calculated for the total thickness of the mineral, are entered on standard record sheets, abbreviated copies of which are reproduced in Appendix F.

Detailed records may be consulted at the appropriate offices of the Institute, upon application to the Head, Industrial Minerals Assessment Unit.

APPENDIX B

STATISTICAL PROCEDURE

Statistical assessment

1 A statistical assessment is made of an area of mineral greater than 2 km², if there is a minimum of five evenly spaced boreholes in the resource block (for smaller areas see paragraph 12 below).

2 The simple methods used in the calculations are consistent with the amount of data provided by the survey. Conventional symmetrical confidence limits are calculated for the 95 per cent probability level, that is, there is a 5 per cent or one in twenty chance of a result falling outside the stated limits.

3 The volume estimate (V) for the mineral in a given block is the product of the two variables, the sampled areas (A) and the mean thickness ($\bar{l}_m$) calculated from the individual thicknesses at the sample points. The standard deviations for these variables are related such that

$$S_V = \sqrt{(S_A^2 + S_{\bar{l}_m}^2)} \qquad [1]$$

4 The above relationship may be transposed such that

$$S_V = S_{\bar{l}_m}\sqrt{(1 + S_A^2/S_{\bar{l}_m}^2)} \qquad [2]$$

From this it can be seen that as $S_A^2/S_{\bar{l}_m}^2$ tends to $0, S_V$ tends to $S_{\bar{l}_m}$.

If, therefore, the standard deviation for area is small with respect to that for mean thickness, the standard deviation for volume approximates to that for mean thickness.

5 Given that the number of approximately evenly spaced sample points in the sampled area is n with mineral thickness measurements $l_{m_1}, l_{m_2}, \ldots l_{m_n}$, then the best estimate of mean thickness, $\bar{l}_m$, is given by

$$\Sigma(l_{m_1} + l_{m_2} \ldots l_{m_n})/n.$$

For groups of closely spaced boreholes a discretionary weighting factor may be applied to avoid bias (see note on weighting below). The standard deviation for mean thickness, $S_{\bar{l}}$, expressed as a proportion of the mean thickness, is given by

$$S_{\bar{l}} = (1/\bar{l}_m)\sqrt{[\Sigma(l_m - \bar{l}_m)^2/(n-1)]}$$

where l_m is any value in the series l_{m_1} to l_{m_n}.

6 The sampled area in each resource block is coloured pink on the map. Wherever possible, calculations relate to the mineral within mapped geological boundaries (which may not necessarily correspond to the limits of deposit). Where the area is not defined by a mapped boundary, that is, where the boundary is inferred, a distinctive symbol is used. Experience suggests that the errors in determining area are small relative to those in thickness. The relationship $S_A/S_{\bar{l}_m} \leq \frac{1}{3}$ is assumed in all cases. It follows from equation [2] that

$$S_{\bar{l}_m} \leq S_V \leq 1.05\, S_{\bar{l}_m} \qquad [3]$$

7 The limits on the estimate of mean thickness of mineral, $L_{\bar{l}_m}$, may be expressed in absolute units $\pm (t/\sqrt{n}) \times S_{\bar{l}_m}$ or as a percentage $\pm (t/\sqrt{n}) \times S_{\bar{l}_m} \times (100/\bar{l}_m)$ per cent, where t is Student's t at the 95 per cent probability level for $(n-1)$ degrees of freedom, evaluated by reference to statistical tables. (In applying Student's t it is assumed that the measurements are distributed normally).

8 Values of t at the 95 per cent probability level for values of n up to 20 are as follows:

n	t	n	t
1	infinity	11	2.228
2	12.706	12	2.201
3	4.303	13	2.179
4	3.182	14	2.160
5	2.776	15	2.145
6	2.571	16	2.131
7	2.447	17	2.120
8	2.365	18	2.110
9	2.306	19	2.101
10	2.262	20	2.093

(from Table 12, Biometrika Tables for Statisticians, Volume 1, Second Edition, Cambridge University Press, 1962). When n is greater than 20, 1.96 is used (the value of t when n is infinity).

9 In calculating confidence limits for volume, L_v, the following inequality corresponding to equation [3] is applied:

$$L\bar{l}_m \leq L_v \leq 1.05 L\bar{l}_m$$

10 In summary, for values of n between 5 and 20, L_v is calculated as

$$[(1.05 \times t)/\bar{l}_m] \times [\sqrt{\Sigma(l_m - \bar{l}_m)^2/n(n-1)}] \times 100$$

per cent, and when n is greater than 20, as

$$[(1.05 \times 1.96)/\bar{l}_m] \times [\sqrt{\Sigma(l_m - \bar{l}_m)^2/n(n-1)}] \times 100$$

per cent. (Weighting factors may be included: see paragraph 15.)

11 The application of this procedure to a fictitious area is illustrated in Figures 10 and 11.

Inferred assessment
12 If the sampled area of mineral in a resource block is between 0.25 km² and 2 km² an assessment is inferred, based on geological and topographical information usually supported by the data from one or two boreholes. The volume of mineral is calculated as the product of the area, measured from field data, and the estimated thickness. Confidence limits are not calculated.

13 In some cases a resource block may include an area left uncoloured on the map, within which mineral (as defined) is interpreted to be generally absent. If there is reason to believe that some mineral may be present, an inferred assessment may be made.

14 No assessment is attempted for an isolated area of mineral less than 0.25 km².

15 *Note on weighting* The thickness of a deposit at any point may be governed solely by the position of the point in relation to a broad trend. However, most sand and gravel deposits also exhibit a random pattern of local, and sometimes considerable, variation in thickness. Thus the distribution of sample points need be only approximately regular and in estimating the mean thickness only simple weighting is necessary. In practice, equal weighting can often be applied to thicknesses at all sample points. If, however, there is a distinctly unequal distribution of points, bias is avoided by dividing the sampled area into broad zones, to each of which a value roughly proportional to its area is assigned. This value is then shared between the data points within the zone as the weighting factor.

APPENDIX C

CLASSIFICATION AND DESCRIPTION OF SAND AND GRAVEL

For the purposes of assessing resources of sand and gravel a classification should take account of economically important characteristics of the deposit, in particular the absolute content of fines and the ratio of sand to gravel.

The terminology commonly used by geologists when describing sedimentary rocks (Wentworth, 1922) is not entirely satisfactory for this purpose. For example, Wentworth proposed that a deposit should be described as a 'gravelly sand' when it contains more sand than gravel and there is at least 10 per cent of gravel, provided that there is less than 10 per cent of material finer than sand (less than $\frac{1}{16}$ mm) and coarser than pebbles (more than 64 mm in diameter). Because deposits containing more than 10 per cent fines are not embraced by this system a modified binary classification based on Willman (1942) has been adopted.

When the fines content exceeds 40 per cent the material is not considered to be potentially workable and falls outside the definition of mineral. Deposits which contain 40 per cent fines or less are classified primarily on the ratio of sand to gravel but qualified in the light of the fines content, as follows: less than 10 per cent fines—no qualification: 10 per cent or more but less than 20 per cent fines—'clayey'; 20 to 40 per cent fines—'very clayey'.

The term 'clay' (as written, with single quote marks) is used to describe all material passing $\frac{1}{16}$ mm. Thus it has no mineralogical significance and includes particles falling within the size range of silt. The normal meaning applies to the term clay where it does not appear in single quotation marks.

The ratio of sand to gravel defines the boundaries between sand, pebbly sand, sandy gravel and gravel (at 19:1, 3:1 and 1:1).

Thus it is possible to classify the mineral into one of twelve descriptive categories (see Figure 12). The procedure is as follows:
1 Classify according to ratio of sand to gravel.
2 Describe fines.
For example, a deposit grading 11 per cent gravel, 70 per cent sand and 19 per cent fines is classified as 'clayey' pebbly sand. This short description is included in the borehole log (see Note 11, Appendix D).

Many differing proposals exist for the classification of the grain size of sediments (Atterberg, 1905; Udden, 1914; Wentworth, 1922; Wentworth, 1935; Allen 1936; Twenhofel, 1937: Lane and others, 1947). As Archer (1970a, b) has emphasised, there is a pressing need for a simple metric scale acceptable to both scientific and engineering interests, for which the class limit sizes correspond closely with certain marked changes in the natural properties of mineral particles. For example, there is an important change in the degree of cohesion between particles at about the $\frac{1}{16}$-mm size, which approximates to the generally accepted boundary between silt and sand. These and other requirements are met by a system based on Udden's geometric scale and a simplified form of Wentworth's terminology (Table 8), which is used in this Report.

The fairly wide intervals in the scale are consistent with the general level of accuracy of the qualitative assessments of the resource blocks. Three sizes of sand are recognised, fine ($+ \frac{1}{16} - \frac{1}{4}$ mm), medium ($+ \frac{1}{4} - 1$ mm) and coarse ($+ 1 - 4$ mm). The boundary at 16 mm distinguishes a range of finer gravel ($+ 4 - 16$ mm), often characterised by abundance of worn tough pebbles of vein-quartz, from larger pebbles often of notably different materials. The boundary at 64 mm distinguishes pebbles from cobbles. The term 'gravel' is used loosely to denote both pebble-sized and cobble-sized material.

The size distribution of borehole samples is determined by sieve analysis, which is presented by the laboratory as logarithmic cumulative curves (see, for example, British Standard 1377: 1967). In this report the grading is tabulated on the borehole record sheets (Appendix F), the intercepts

Block calculation 1:25 000 } Fictitious
Block

Area
Block: 11.08 km²
Mineral: 8.32 km²

Mean thickness
Overburden: 2.5 m
Mineral: 6.5 m

Volume
Overburden: 21 million m³
Mineral: 54 million m³

Confidence limits of the estimate of mineral volume at the
95 per cent probability level: ± 20 per cent
That is, the volume of mineral (with 95 per cent probability):
54 ± 11 million m³

Thickness estimate measurements in metres
l_o = overburden thickness l_m = mineral thickness

Sample point	Weighting w	Overburden		Mineral		Remarks
		l_o	wl_o	l_m	wl_m	
SE 14	1	1.5	1.5	9.4	9.4	
SE 18	1	3.3	3.3	5.8	5.8	
SE 20	1	nil	–	6.9	6.9	IMAU
SE 22	1	0.7	0.7	6.4	6.4	boreholes
SE 23	1	6.2	6.2	4.1	4.1	
SE 24	1	4.3	4.3	6.4	6.4	
SE 17	½	1.2 } 1.6		9.8 } 7.2		Hydrogeology
123/45	½	2.0		4.6		Unit record
1	¼	2.7 ⎤		7.3 ⎤		Close group
2	¼	4.5 ⎥ 2.6		3.2 ⎥ 5.8		of four
3	¼	0.4 ⎥		6.8 ⎥		boreholes
4	¼	2.8 ⎦		5.9 ⎦		(commercial)
Totals	$\Sigma w = 8$	$\Sigma wl_o = 20.2$		$\Sigma wl_m = 52.0$		
Means		$w\bar{l}_o = 2.5$		$w\bar{l}_m = 6.5$		

Calculation of confidence limits

wl_m	$(wl_m - w\bar{l}_m)$	$(wl_m - w\bar{l}_m)^2$
9.4	2.9	8.41
5.8	0.7	0.49
6.9	0.4	0.16
6.4	0.1	0.01
4.1	2.4	5.76
6.4	0.1	0.01
7.2	0.7	0.49
5.8	0.7	0.49

$\Sigma(wl_m - w\bar{l}_m)^2 = 15.82$
$n = 8$
$t = 2.365$

L_v is calculated as

$1.05(t/w\bar{l}_m)\sqrt{[\Sigma(wl_m - w\bar{l}_m)^2/n(n-1)]} \times 100$

$= 1.05 \times (2.365/6.5)\sqrt{[15.82/(8 \times 7)]} \times 100$

$= 20.3$

$\simeq$ 20 per cent

Figure 10 Example of resource block assessment:
calculation and results.

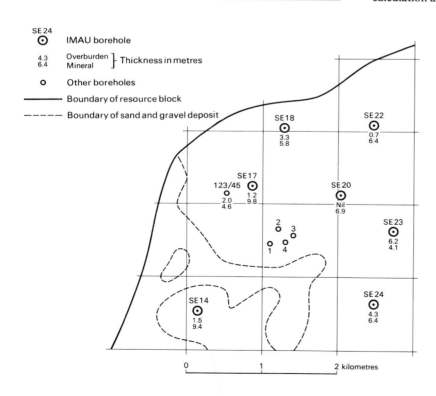

SE 24 ⊙ IMAU borehole

4.3 / 6.4 Overburden } Thickness in metres
Mineral

o Other boreholes

—— Boundary of resource block

----- Boundary of sand and gravel deposit

SE 18 ⊙ 3.3 / 5.8

SE 22 ⊙ 0.7 / 6.4

SE 17 123/45 ⊙ o 2.0 / 4.6 1.2 / 9.8

SE 20 ⊙ Nil / 6.9

SE 23 ⊙ 6.2 / 4.1

2 o 3 o o 1 o 4

SE 14 ⊙ 1.5 / 9.4

SE 24 ⊙ 4.3 / 6.4

0   1   2 kilometres

Figure 11 Example of resource block assessment: map of fictitious block.

18

corresponding with the simple geometric scale $\frac{1}{16}$ mm, $\frac{1}{4}$ mm, 1 mm, 4 mm, 16 mm and so on as required. Original sample grading curves are available for reference at the appropriate office of the Institute.

Each bulk sample is described, subjectively, by a geologist at the borehole site. Being based on visual examination, the description of the grading is inexact, the accuracy depending on the experience of the observer. The descriptions recorded are modified, as necessary, when the laboratory results become available.

The relative proportions of the rock types present in the gravel fraction are indicated by the use of the words 'and' or 'with'. For example, 'flint and quartz' indicates very approximate equal proportions with neither constituent accounting for less than about 25 per cent of the whole; 'flint with quartz' indicates that flint is dominant and quartz, the principal accessory rock type, comprises 5 to 25 per cent of the whole. Where the accessory material accounts for less than 5 per cent of the whole, but is still readily apparent, the phrase 'with some' has been used. Rare constituents are referred to as 'trace'.

The terms used in the field to describe the degree of rounding of particles, which is concerned with the sharpness of the edges and corners of a clastic fragment and not the shape (after Pettjohn, 1975), are as follows.

Angular: showing little or no evidence of wear; sharp edges and corners.

Subangular: showing definite effects of wear. Fragments still have their original form but edges and corners begin to be rounded off.

Subrounded: showing considerable wear. The edges and corners are rounded off to smooth curves. Original grain shape is still distinct.

Rounded: original faces almost completely destroyed, but some comparatively flat surfaces may still remain. All original edges and corners have been smoothed off to rather broad curves. Original shape is still apparent.

Well-rounded: no original faces, edges or corners left. The entire surface consists of broad curves; flat areas are absent. The original shape is suggested by the present form of the grain.

Table 8 Classification of gravel, sand and fines

Size limits	Grain size description	Qualification	Primary classification
64 mm –	Cobble		
		Coarse	Gravel
16 mm –	Pebble		
		Fine	
4 mm –			
		Coarse	
1 mm –			
	Sand	Medium	Sand
$\frac{1}{4}$ mm –			
		Fine	
$\frac{1}{16}$ mm –			
	Fines (silt and clay)		Fines

I   Gravel

II   'Clayey' gravel

III   'Very clayey' gravel

IV   Sandy gravel

V   'Clayey' sandy gravel

VI   'Very clayey' sandy gravel

VII   Pebbly sand

VIII   'Clayey' pebbly sand

IX   'Very clayey' pebbly sand

X   Sand

XI   'Clayey' sand

XII   'Very clayey' sand

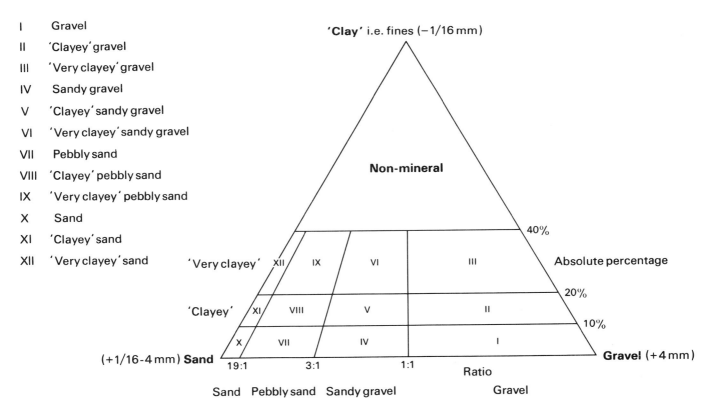

Figure 12 Diagram to show the descriptive categories used in the classification of sand and gravel.

APPENDIX D
EXPLANATION OF THE BOREHOLE RECORDS
Annotated example

SU 58 SE 5[1]   **5962 8043**[2]   **Near Elmcroft, Goring**[3]   **Block B**

Surface level (c. +42.7 m) c. +140 ft[4]   [7]Overburden 1.8 m
Water struck at (c. +40.9 m)[5]   Mineral 3.1 m
Shell and auger, 8 in (203 mm) diameter[6]   Bedrock 0.6 m +[9]
September 1975

LOG

Geological classification	Lithology	Thickness m	Depth[8] m
	Soil, clayey and silty; black	0.2	0.2
Alluvium	Clay, silty and soft, faintly mottled in grey; brown	1.6	1.8
River Terrace Deposits (First Terrace)[10]	Gravel, becoming sandier with depth[11]	3.1	4.9
	Gravel; fine to coarse with cobbles (mainly flint), mainly well rounded buff to brown limestone, with sub-angular to subrounded black and white coated (patina) flint, soft white chalk pellets and brownish black ironstone, occasional well rounded white quartz, and reddish brown quartzite. Flint predominates in the coarse fraction (+16 mm)		
	Sand: medium and coarse with some fine, mainly quartz, flint and chalk; chalk content increases with depth; light brown		
Middle Chalk	Chalk, soft with occasional flint; white	0.6+	5.5

GRADING

Mean for deposit[14] *percentages*			Depth below surface (m)[12]	*percentages[13]*						
Fines	Sand	Gravel		Fines	Sand			Gravel		
				$-\frac{1}{16}$	$+\frac{1}{16}-\frac{1}{4}$	$+\frac{1}{4}-1$	$+1-4$	$+4-16$	$+16-64$	$+64$
2	44	54	*1.8–2.8[15]	3	1	13	19	32	26	6
			*2.8–3.8	1	3	19	19	30	28	0
			*3.8–4.9	2	6	27	25	29	10	1
			Mean	2	3	20	21	31	21	2

COMPOSITION

Depth below surface (m)	Percentages (in +4−16 mm fraction)[16]					
	Flint	Quartz and quartzite[17]	Limestone	Chalk[18]	Ironstone[19]	Minor constituents[20]
1.8–2.8	8	8	63	3	18	—
2.8–3.8	20	6	52	6	16	—
3.8–4.9	22	4	43	25	6	—
Mean	17	6	52	12	13	—
	Percentages (in +16 mm fraction)					
1.8–2.8	69	2	9	—	1	—
2.8–3.8	68	29	2	1	—	—
3.8–4.9	70	—	—	30	—	—
Mean[22]	69	16	4	11	tr[21]	—

20

The numbered paragraphs below correspond with the annotations given on the specimen record.

1 Borehole Registration Number
Each Industrial Minerals Assessment Unit (IMAU) borehole is identified by a Registration Number. This consists of two statements:

1 The number of the 1:25 000 sheet on which the borehole lies, for example SU 58

2 The quarter of the 1:25 000 sheet on which the borehole lies and its number in a series for that quarter, for example SE 5

Thus the full Registration Number is SU 58 SE 5. Usually this is abbreviated to 58 SE 5 in the text.

2 The National Grid reference
All National Grid references in this publication lie within the 100-km square SU unless otherwise stated. Grid references are given to eight figures, accurate to within 10 m for borehole locations. (In the text, six-figure grid references are used for more approximate locations, for example, for gravel pits.)

3 Location
The position of the borehole is generally referred to the nearest named locality on the 1:25 000 base map and the resource block in which it lies is stated.

4 Surface level
The surface level at the borehole site is given in metres and feet above Ordnance Datum. Measurements were made in feet and approximate conversions are given in brackets. Where the surface level has been estimated, it is prefixed by the letter 'c' (circa).

5 Groundwater conditions
If groundwater was present the level at which it was encountered is normally given (in metres above Ordnance Datum).

6 Type of drill and date of drilling
Modified shell and auger rigs were used in this survey. The type of machine used, the external diameter of the casing, and the month and year of completion of the borehole are stated.

7 Overburden, mineral, waste and bedrock
Mineral is sand and gravel which, as part of a deposit, falls within the arbitrary definition of potentially workable material (see p.1). Bedrock is the 'formation', 'country rock' or 'rock head' below which potentially workable sand and gravel will not be found. Waste is any material other than bedrock or mineral. Where waste occurs between the surface and mineral it is classified as overburden.

8 Thickness and Depth
Measurements were made in metres.

9 The plus sign (+) indicates that the base of the deposit was not reached during drilling.

10 Geological classification
The geological classification is given whenever possible.

11 Lithological description
When sand and gravel is recorded a general description based on the mean grading characteristics (for details see Appendix C) is followed by more detailed particulars. The description of other rocks is based on visual examination in the field.

12 Sampling
A continuous series of bulk samples is taken throughout the thickness of sand and gravel. A new sample is commenced whenever there is an appreciable lithological change within the sand and gravel or at every 1 m of depth.

13 Grading results
The limits are as follows: gravel, $+4$ mm; sand, $+\frac{1}{16}$ mm -4 mm; fines, $-\frac{1}{16}$ mm.

14 Mean grading
The grading of the full thickness of the mineral horizon identified in the log is the mean of the individual sample gradings weighted by the thicknesses represented, if these vary. The classification used is shown in Table 8. Fully representative sampling of sand and gravel is difficult to achieve, particularly where groundwater levels are high. Comparison between boreholes and adjacent exposures suggests that in borehole samples the proportion of sand may be higher and the proportions of fines and coarse gravel ($+16$ mm) may be lower.

15 Bailed samples
Samples obtained by the bailing technique (that is, from deposits below the water table) are indicated by an asterisk.

16 Composition results
Details are given of the composition on a percentage by weight basis of each of the constituents in the $+4 -16$ mm (fine gravel) fraction for each of the original bulk samples, and for some bulk samples in the $+16$ mm fraction.

17 This component includes mostly 'Bunter'-derived material. Counted with the quartzites are Bunter sandstones. In some bulk samples quartz and quartzite (including sandstones) have been separately assessed.

18 In some bulk samples limestone and chalk have been assessed together because of their close similarities in appearance and properties; where possible the chalk has been separately counted.

19 This component occasionally includes, in addition to ironstone, ironpan, iron-cemented sandstones, oolitic ironstone and iron-stained flints.

20 Minor constituents include glauconitic siltstones (marl), puddingstones, sarsens, lydites, cherts, fossils, and igneous, metamorphic and sedimentary rocks.

21 'tr' indicates trace. This means that the component is present in quantities of less than 1 per cent.

22 Mean composition
The composition of the full thickness of the mineral horizon identified in the log is the mean of the individual samples which have previously been weighted with respect to thickness and sample weight.

APPENDIX E

LIST OF INDUSTRIAL MINERALS ASSESSMENT UNIT BOREHOLES AND EXPOSURES USED IN THE ASSESSMENT OF RESOURCES

Borehole number*	Grid references†	Borehole number*	Grid reference†	Borehole number*	Grid reference†
1 IMAU BOREHOLES		11	6013 8896	11	6957 8061
		12	6106 8729	12	6954 8285
(pp.23-40)		13	6098 8512	13‡	6944 8436
58 NE 1	5579 8717	14	6449 8967		
2	5655 8960	15	6400 8800		
3	5616 8839	16	6145 897 5		
4	5679 8747	17‡	6108 8562		
5	5646 8651	18‡	6413 8919	**2** OTHER BOREHOLES	
6	5709 8869	19	6379 8582	**a** 1 Central and South Midlands Unit	
7	5737 8580	20‡	6386 8650	borehole (included amongst Industrial	
8	5902 8932			Minerals Assessment Unit boreholes :	
9	5840 8778			Appendix F, p.23)	
10	5851 8758	(pp.59-66)			
11	5821 8706	68 SW 1	6049 8285	58 NE 16	5826 8617
12	5960 8850	2	6164 8363		
13	5971 8837	3	6170 8019	**b** 18 Hydrogeology Unit Records (not	
14	5928 8776	4	6377 8077	quoted in Appendix F)	
15	5967 8578	5	6255 8187	58 NE 22	5997 8922
16	5826 8617	6	6350 8220	58 NE 25	5978 8610
17	5756 8962	7	6483 8272	58 NE 30	5986 8757
18	5853 8639	8	6450 8065	58 NE 38	5976 8928
19	5962 8682	9	6046 8413	58 SE 13	5927 8373
20	5985 8697	10	6179 8288	68 NW 1	6178 8998
		11	6171 8204	68 NW 2	6172 8970
(pp.41-45)				68 NW 3	6132 8991
58 SE 2	5979 8422	(pp. 67-77)		68 NW 21	6460 8882
3	5965 8324	68 SE 1	6955 8235	68 NW 23	6382 8820
4	5964 8235	2	6863 8208	68 NW 26	6003 8505
5	5962 8043	3	6754 8135	68 NW 31	6410 8592
26‡	5779 8453	4	6707 8225	68 NW 34	6019 8956
		5	6614 8117	68 NW 35	6062 8922
(pp.46-58)		6	6629 8287	68 SW 19	6044 8458
68 NW 8	6030 8845	7	6523 8180	68 SW 25	6023 8026
9	6032 8745	8	6683 8083	68 SE 16	6797 8408
10	6040 8575	9	6757 8042	68 SE 18	6828 8249
		10	6859 8082		

* By sheet quadrant
† All fall within 100-km square SU
‡ These are sites where exposures in gravel pits or pipe-line trenches enabled measurement to be accurately taken and samples collected at every metre.

APPENDIX F

INDUSTRIAL MINERALS ASSESSMENT UNIT BOREHOLE AND EXPOSURE RECORDS

SU 58 NE 1   5579 8717   Ham Farm, Ashton Upthorpe

Surface level (+50.9 m) +167 ft
Water not struck
Shell and auger, 6 in (152 mm) diameter
November 1971

Waste 0.8 m
Bedrock 0.6 m +

LOG

Geological classification	Lithology	Thickness m	Depth m
	Soil, with occasional rounded quartzite pebbles; dark brown	0.3	0.3
	Subsoil, silty clay with occasional subangular flint and well rounded quartzite pebbles; dark to light brown	0.5	0.8
Upper Greensand	Clay, silty with marl fragments; light yellowish green	0.2	1.0
	Marl, silty, becoming hard and 'blocky'; pale green	0.4+	1.4

Surface level (+47.9 m) +157 ft
Water struck at (+46.2 m)
Shell and auger, 6 in (152 mm) diameter
December 1971

Overburden 2.4 m
Mineral 5.8 m
Bedrock 0.5+ m

LOG

Geological classification	Lithology	Thickness m	Depth m
	Soil, silty clay with shells and peat; brown	0.3	0.3
Alluvium	Clay, silty in parts with occasional reddish brown ironstone seam; light greenish brown	1.0	1.3
	Silt, sandy with occasional gravel, glauconitic in parts; greenish grey	1.1	2.4

River Terrace Deposits (First Terrace)	Sandy gravel, with silt seams in upper 0.5 m
	  Gravel: fine to coarse, dominantly subrounded to rounded oolitic limestone, some subangular to subrounded flint, subrounded brown ironstone, occasional rounded reddish brown quartzite and chalk
	  Sand: medium with coarse and some fine, mainly quartz and limestone, occasionally glauconitic; brown
		5.8	8.2

Upper Greensand	Silt, with rare pebbles; light green becoming bluish grey	0.5+	8.7

GRADING

Mean for deposit percentages			Depth below surface (m)	percentages						
Fines	Sand	Gravel		Fines	Sand			Gravel		
				$-\frac{1}{16}$	$+\frac{1}{16}-\frac{1}{4}$	$+\frac{1}{4}-1$	$+1-4$	$+4-16$	$+16-64$	$+64$
16	47	37	*2.4–2.9	58	0	12	10	17	3	0
			*2.9–3.9	26	15	42	11	5	1	0
			*3.9–4.9	13	5	46	10	12	14	0
			*4.9–5.9	4	0	25	17	30	24	0
			*5.9–6.9	7	1	33	29	21	9	0
			*6.9–8.2	11	1	14	5	48	21	0
			Mean	16	4	29	14	24	13	0

COMPOSITION

Depth below surface (m)	Percentages (in +4–16 mm fraction)				
	Flint	Quartz and quartzite	Limestone	Chalk	Ironstone
2.4–2.9	24	—	67	—	9
2.9–3.9	16	7	75	—	2
3.9–4.9	5	1	68	6	20
4.9–5.9	12	2	67	2	17
5.9–6.9	11	6	69	—	14
6.9–8.2	8	4	77	—	11
Mean	12	3	71	2	12

Surface level (+53.0 m) +174 ft
Water not struck
Shell and auger, 6 in (152 mm) diameter
December 1971

Waste 2.5 m
Bedrock 1.1 m +

LOG

Geological classification	Lithology	Thickness m	Depth m
	Soil, clayey with occasional well rounded quartz pebbles	0.2	0.2
River Terrace Deposits (Second Terrace)	Clay, silty, becoming pebbly and sandy towards the base; greenish brown	2.3	2.5
Upper Greensand	Silt and clay, becoming compact and hard; light grey to greyish green	1.1+	3.6

Surface level (+49.1 m) 161 ft
Water not struck at (+47.6 m)
Shell and auger, 6 in (152 mm) diameter
November 1971

Overburden 0.8 m
Mineral 1.0 m
Waste 1.8 m
Mineral 4.5 m
Bedrock 0.7 m +

LOG

Geological classification	Lithology	Thickness m	Depth m
	Soil, dark brown	0.4	0.4
Alluvium	Clay, stiff, with occasional white fragile gastropod shells and chalk pellets, mottled brown and reddish brown; grey to pale green	0.4	0.8

River Terrace Deposits (First Terrace)	Sandy gravel
	    Gravel: fine dominantly subrounded chalk, with occasional subangular to subrounded flint.
	    Sand: fine to medium, silty, mainly chalk with some chalk and glauconite; light green
		1.0	1.8

	Silt, sandy and very glauconitic with occasional fine chalk pellets; dark green	1.8	3.6

	Sandy gravel
	    Gravel: fine to coarse, mainly well rounded chalk and subrounded to rounded, grey, brown and bluish grey shelly and oolitic limestone; some subrounded flint reddish brown ironstone, occasional rounded reddish brown quartzite, traces of sandstone and worn shell fragments
	    Sand: medium with coarse and some fine, very glauconitic, mainly quartz and limestone; greyish green
		4.5	8.1

Upper Greensand	Silt, micaceous and glauconitic; green	0.4	8.5
	Siltstone, hard and blocky; green	0.3+	8.8

GRADING

	Mean for deposit percentages			Depth below surface (m)	percentages						
	Fines	Sand	Gravel		Fines	Sand			Gravel		
					$-\frac{1}{16}$	$+\frac{1}{16}-\frac{1}{4}$	$+\frac{1}{4}-1$	$+1-4$	$+4-16$	$+16-64$	$+64$
a	21	56	23	0.8–1.8	21	12	27	17	22	1	0
b	6	59	35	*3.6–4.6	7	15	37	15	24	2	0
				*4.6–5.6	7	1	48	24	18	2	0
				*5.6–6.6	7	3	36	18	25	11	0
				*6.6–7.6	4	2	30	17	30	17	0
				*7.6–8.1	2	4	16	28	37	13	0
				Mean	6	5	34	20	26	9	0
a+b	9	59	32	Mean	9	6	34	19	25	7	0

COMPOSITION

Depth below surface (m)	Percentages (in +4−16 mm fraction)				
	Flint	Quartz and quartzite	Limestone	Chalk	Ironstone
0.8–1.8	7	—	—	93	—
3.6–4.6	19	4	4	59	14
4.6–5.6	16	4	66	7	7
5.6–6.6	22	6	55	9	8
6.6–7.6	7	1	71	8	13
7.6–8.1	9	3	71	11	6
Mean	14	3	44	31	8

Surface level (+48.8 m) 160 ft   Overburden 1.3 m
Water struck at (+47.6 m)   Mineral 4.3 m
Shell and auger, 6 in (152 mm) diameter   Bedrock 0.4 m +
November 1971

LOG

Geological classification	Lithology	Thickness m	Depth m
Made ground	Soil, and siltstone fragments; brown	0.5	0.5
Alluvium	Silt and clay, with occasional pebbles of chalk, flint and quartz; brown to pale greyish green	0.8	1.3
River Terrace Deposits (First Terrace)	'Clayey' sandy gravel, with clay seam between 4.3 and 4.7 m Gravel: fine to coarse with occasional cobbles (of quartzite), dominantly well rounded chalk with subrounded to rounded brown oolitic limestone; occasional well rounded reddish brown quartzite, subangular to rounded flint and reddish brown ironstone, traces of siltstone Sand: fine to coarse, silty and clayey throughout, very glauconitic, mainly quartz and limestone with some ironstone and chalk; light brown to greenish brown	4.3	5.6
Upper Greensand	Silt, dense and compact with siltstone fragments, glauconitic; light green	0.4+	6.0

GRADING

Mean for deposit *percentages*			Depth below surface (m)	*percentages*						
Fines	Sand	Gravel		Fines	Sand			Gravel		
				$-\frac{1}{16}$	$+\frac{1}{16}-\frac{1}{4}$	$+\frac{1}{4}-1$	$+1-4$	$+4-16$	$+16-64$	$+64$
12	44	44	*1.3–2.3	20	25	17	12	23	3	0
			*2.3–3.3	10	21	15	11	29	14	0
			*3.3–4.3	13	11	14	11	27	24	0
			*4.7–5.6	5	1	18	19	37	20	0
			Mean	12	15	16	13	29	15	0

COMPOSITION

Depth below surface (m)	Percentages (in +4−16 mm fraction)					
	Flint	Quartz and quartzite	Limestone	Chalk	Ironstone	Minor constituents
1.3–2.3	1	5	—	94	—	—
2.3–3.3	1	1	—	95	3	—
3.3−4.3	2	9	16	63	8	2
4.7−5.6	14	2	58	10	15	1
Mean	5	4	18	66	6	1

Surface level (+47.5 m) +156 ft
Water struck at (+44.9 m)
Shell and auger, 6 in (152 mm) diameter
September 1972

Overburden 1.7 m
Mineral 1.0 m
Waste 1.0 m
Mineral 4.2 m
Bedrock 0.1 m+

LOG

Geological classification	Lithology	Thickness m	Depth m
	Soil	0.2	0.2
Alluvium	Clay, very sandy with pebbles of subangular white flint and well rounded quartzite, slightly glauconitic; brown	1.2	1.4
	Silt, clayey with occasional flint pebbles, brown and dark grey	0.3	1.7

River Terrace Deposits (First Terrace)	'Clayey' sandy gravel
	    Gravel: fine to coarse, dominantly subangular flint and subrounded oolitic limestone, with some quartz and quartzite and ironstone; traces of subrounded green siltstone
	    Sand: very silty, glauconitic; dark greenish grey
		1.0	2.7

	Clay and silt, with occasional flint and limestone pebbles; dark greenish grey	1.0	3.7

	'Clayey' sandy gravel
	    Gravel: fine to coarse with occasional cobble (of flint), mainly subrounded, ovoid to platy, brown oolitic and shelly limestone, and subangular to subrounded flint; occasional well rounded quartzite and reddish brown ironstone, rare well rounded white vein-quartz; trace of green siltstone
	    Sand: medium to coarse with some fine, mainly quartz with flint and some ironstone; greyish brown
		4.2	7.9

Upper Greensand	Siltstone, hard, platy and shaly; dark grey	0.1+	8.0

GRADING

	Mean for deposit *percentages*			Depth below surface (m)	*percentages*						
	Fines	Sand	Gravel		Fines	Sand			Gravel		
					$-\frac{1}{16}$	$+\frac{1}{16}-\frac{1}{4}$	$+\frac{1}{4}-1$	$+1-4$	$+4-16$	$+16-64$	$+64$
a	39	33	28	0.7–2.7	39	5	20	8	21	7	0
b	6	50	44	*3.7–4.7	7	3	36	13	29	12	0
				*4.7–5.7	11	2	36	21	26	4	0
				*5.7–6.7	2	2	22	21	38	15	0
				*6.7–7.9	5	1	23	22	27	22	0
				Mean	6	2	29	19	30	14	0
a+b	17	45	38	Mean	17	3	26	16	26	12	0

COMPOSITION

Depth below surface (m)	Percentages (in +4−16 mm fraction)			
	Flint	Quartz and quartzite	Limestone and chalk	Ironstone
1.7–2.7	37	1	57	5
3.7–4.7	8	4	84	4
4.7–5.7	13	4	75	8
5.7–6.7	12	4	71	13
6.7–7.9	7	18	59	16
Mean	16	6	69	9

Surface level (+ 48.5 m) + 159 ft   Waste 1.2 m
Water struck at (+ 46.8 m)   Bedrock 1.8 m +
Shell and auger, 6 in (152 mm) diameter
September 1972

LOG

Geological classification	Lithology	Thickness m	Depth m
	Soil	0.3	0.3
Alluvium	Clay, silty in parts; greyish green	0.9	1.2
Lower Chalk (Glauconitic Marl)	Silt, chalky with occasional siltstone, soft becoming compact and hard; greyish green	1.8+	3.0

Surface level (+47.2 m) +155 ft   Overburden 1.1 m
Water struck at (+45.6 m)   Mineral 5.7 m
Shell and auger, 6 in (152 mm) diameter   Bedrock 0.3 m +
September 1972

LOG

Geological classification	Lithology	Thickness m	Depth m
	Soil, slightly pebbly; dark brown	0.3	0.3
Alluvium	Clay, silty becoming sandy, occasional subangular flint, rounded reddish brown quartzite, rounded white quartz and friable light grey siltstone	0.8	1.1

River Terrace Deposits (First Terrace)	'Clayey' gravel, becoming progressively more gravelly with depth
	  Gravel: fine to coarse, dominantly subrounded brown oolitic and shelly oolitic limestone, with some subangular flint, well rounded brown quartzite, well rounded white quartz and ironstone; traces of green siltstone and chalk
	  Sand: medium and coarse with occasional fine, mainly quartz, flint, hematite and glauconite; greyish brown
		5.7	6.8

Upper Greensand	Siltstone, dense, partly shaly; dark greenish grey	0.3+	7.1

GRADING

Mean for deposit *percentages*			Depth below surface (m)	*percentages*							
Fines	Sand	Gravel		Fines	Sand				Gravel		
				$-\frac{1}{16}$	$+\frac{1}{16}-\frac{1}{4}$	$+\frac{1}{4}-1$	$+1-4$		$+4-16$	$+16-64$	$+64$
10	43	47	1.1–2.1	33	4	25	13		23	2	0
			*2.1–3.1	12	3	28	20		27	10	0
			*3.1–4.1	8	2	20	19		41	10	0
			*4.1–5.1	3	2	24	24		39	8	0
			*5.1–6.1	2	1	11	25		35	26	0
			*6.1–6.8	2	2	14	16		35	31	0
			Mean	10	2	21	20		33	14	0

COMPOSITION

Depth below surface (m)	Percentages (in +4−16 mm fraction)				
	Flint	Quartz and quartzite	Limestone	Chalk	Ironstone
1.1–2.1	22	18	61	2	7
2.1–3.1	15	6	69	1	9
3.1–4.1	8	5	76	tr	11
4.1–5.1	12	2	78	tr	8
5.1–6.1	6	5	76	2	11
6.1–6.8	13	5	65	—	17
Mean	12	5	72	1	10

SU 58 NE 9   5840 8778   Hillgreen Farm, Cholsey

Surface level (+55.2 m) +181 ft   Waste 0.4 m
Water not struck   Bedrock 1.6 m +
Shell and auger, 6 in (152 mm) diameter
December 1971

LOG

Geological classification	Lithology	Thickness m	Depth m
	Soil, clayey with well rounded reddish brown quartzite pebbles; dark brown	0.2	0.2
	Subsoil, silty clay; olive-green to brown	0.2	0.4
Upper Greensand	Clay, silty with weathered subangular to subrounded siltstone fragments; light brown to olive-green	0.9	1.3
	Silt, becoming compact and hard with depth; uniformly pale green	0.7+	2.0

SU 58 NE 10   5851 8758   Hillgreen Farm, Cholsey

Surface level (+51.2 m) +168 ft   Waste 0.2 m
Water not struck   Bedrock 2.0 m +
Shell and auger, 6 in (152 mm) diameter
December 1971

LOG

Geological classification	Lithology	Thickness m	Depth m
	Soil, clayey with reddish brown quartzite pebbles; dark brown	0.2	0.2
Upper Greensand	Clay, silty with subangular fragments of argillaceous siltstone becoming hard with depth; olive-green becoming light green	1.2	1.4
	Silt, dense and hard; uniformly light green	0.8+	2.2

Surface level (+52.4 m) +172 ft
Water not struck
Shell and auger, 6 in (152 mm) diameter
December 1971

Overburden 0.8 m
Mineral 1.4 m
Bedrock 0.3 m +

LOG

Geological classification	Lithology	Thickness m	Depth m
	Soil, with occasional rounded reddish brown quartzite; dark brown	0.2	0.2
River Terrace Deposits (Second Terrace)	Clay, sandy with occasional rounded reddish brown quartzite, rounded white quartz and subangular flint; orange-brown	0.6	0.8

	'Clayey' sandy gravel
	    Gravel: fine to coarse, dominantly subrounded brown limestone, occasional subangular to subrounded flint, rounded reddish brown quartzite, subrounded white chalk and subrounded brown ironstone; trace of green siltstone
	    Sand: medium with coarse and some fine, mainly quartz and limestone; brown
		1.4	2.2

Upper Greensand	Siltstone, dense and hard, some brown iron staining; pale green	0.3+	2.5

GRADING

Mean for deposit *percentages*			Depth below surface (m)	*percentages*						
Fines	Sand	Gravel		Fines	Sand			Gravel		
				$-\frac{1}{16}$	$+\frac{1}{16}-\frac{1}{4}$	$+\frac{1}{4}-1$	$+1-4$	$+4-16$	$+16-64$	$+64$
13	53	34	0.8–2.2	13	6	28	19	28	6	0

COMPOSITION

Depth below surface (m)	Percentages (in $+4-16$ mm fraction)				
	Flint	Quartz and quartzite	Limestone	Chalk	Ironstone
0.8–2.2	9	5	68	9	9

SU 58 NE 12   **5960 8850**   **Old Hithercroft Farm, Cholsey**

Surface level (+47.2 m) +155 ft
Water not struck
Shell and auger, 6 in (152 mm) diameter
September 1972

Waste 0.3 m
Bedrock 0.7 m +

LOG

Geological classification	Lithology	Thickness m	Depth m
	Soil, brown	0.1	0.1
	Subsoil, silty clay, slightly sandy with occasional subangular to subrounded green siltstone fragments; light greyish brown	0.2	0.3
Lower Chalk	Siltstone, very chalky, becoming harder and firmer with depth; uniformly light greyish green	0.7+	1.0

Surface level (+46.9 m) +154 ft
Water struck at (+43.7 m)
Shell and auger, 6 in (152 mm) diameter
September 1972

Overburden 0.7 m
Mineral 5.1 m
Bedrock 0.3 m+

LOG

Geological classification	Lithology	Thickness m	Depth m
	Soil, with scattered well rounded pebbles of flint, brown quartzite and white quartz; dark brown	0.1	0.1
River Terrace Deposits (First Terrace)	Clay, very silty, becoming chalky towards the base, with scattered pebbles of green siltstone and well rounded brown quartzite and quartz; greyish brown	0.6	0.7
	'Clayey' sandy gravel	5.1	5.8
	Gravel: fine with some coarse, dominantly brown subrounded tabular to platy oolitic and shelly limestone, with some subangular brown and black flint, brown ironstone and occasional well rounded brown quartzite and well rounded white quartz; traces of green siltstone, white chalk pellets and worn shell fragments		
	Sand: medium with coarse and some fine, mainly quartz; flint and chalk; silty in parts; horizon of mainly sand (94 per cent) between 2.7 and 3.6 m; light brown		
Lower Chalk	Siltstone, very chalky; light green	0.3+	6.1

GRADING

Mean for deposit *percentages*			Depth below surface (m)	*percentages*							
Fines	Sand	Gravel		Fines	Sand				Gravel		
				$-\frac{1}{16}$	$+\frac{1}{16}-\frac{1}{4}$	$+\frac{1}{4}-1$	$+1-4$	$+4-16$	$+16-64$	$+64$
16	61	23	0.7–1.7	20	5	24	18	28	5	0
			1.7–2.7	32	3	37	16	11	1	0
			*2.7–3.6	0	34	44	16	6	0	0
			*3.6–4.6	18	5	32	19	24	2	0
			*4.6–5.8	8	7	33	18	29	5	0
			Mean	16	10	34	17	20	3	0

COMPOSITION

Depth below surface (m)	Percentages (in +4−16 mm fraction)			
	Flint	Quartz and quartzite	Limestone and chalk	Ironstone
0.7–1.7	9	8	67	16
1.7–2.7	11	6	70	13
2.7–3.6	13	9	64	14
3.6–4.6	17	4	72	7
4.6–5.8	20	9	52	19
Mean	14	7	65	14

Surface level (+46.3 m) +152 ft
Water struck at (+45.5 m)
Shell and auger, 6 in (152 mm) diameter
December 1971

Overburden 0.6 m
Mineral 6.2 m+
Bedrock 0.2 m+

LOG

Geological classification	Lithology	Thickness m	Depth m
	Soil, clayey; dark brown	0.2	0.2
River Terrace Deposits (First Terrace)	Clay, silty, with occasional reddish brown iron concentrations and patches of iron staining; light brown to pale grey	0.4	0.6
	Sandy gravel	6.2	6.8
	Gravel: fine to coarse, dominantly subrounded brown limestone with subangular to subrounded flint, subrounded white chalk, and subrounded reddish brown ironstone, occasional rounded white quartz and a trace of subrounded green siltstone		
	Sand: medium to coarse with some fine, mainly quartz, limestone, flint and some glauconite; buff to greenish grey		
Lower Chalk (Glauconitic Marl)	Siltstone, hard argillaceous, occasionally stained reddish brown; light greyish green	0.2+	7.0

GRADING

Mean for deposit *percentages*			Depth below surface (m)	*percentages*						
Fines	Sand	Gravel		Fines	Sand			Gravel		
				$-\frac{1}{16}$	$+\frac{1}{16}-\frac{1}{4}$	$+\frac{1}{4}-1$	$+1-4$	$+4-16$	$+16-64$	$+64$
5	53	42	0.6–1.5	20	17	24	12	23	4	0
			*1.5–2.5	3	3	16	26	47	5	0
			*2.5–3.5	3	3	24	23	34	13	0
			*3.5–4.5	2	6	35	22	27	8	0
			*4.5–5.5	0	2	20	26	40	12	0
			*5.5–6.8	2	3	17	39	31	8	0
			Mean	5	5	22	26	34	8	0

COMPOSITION

Depth below surface (m)	Percentages (in +4−16 mm fraction)					
	Flint	Quartz and quartzite	Limestone	Chalk	Ironstone	Minor constituents
0.6–1.5	18	3	56	21	—	2
1.5–2.5	19	3	68	5	4	1
2.5–3.5	12	2	68	6	12	—
3.5–4.5	5	3	64	17	10	1
4.5–5.5	8	2	70	10	10	—
5.5–6.8	9	4	56	19	10	2
Mean	12	3	64	12	8	1

Surface level (+49.7 m) +163 ft
Water struck at (+44.3 m)
Shell and auger, 6 in (152 mm) diameter
December 1971

Overburden 1.1 m
Mineral 4.3 m
Bedrock 0.3 m +

LOG

Geological classification	Lithology	Thickness m	Depth m
	Soil, with reddish brown quartzite pebbles; dark brown	0.2	0.2
River Terrace Deposits (First Terrace)	Clay, sandy becoming very sandy with occasional rounded quartz, quartzite and flint pebbles	0.9	1.1
	'Clayey' gravel	4.3	5.4
	Gravel: fine to coarse, mainly well rounded brown limestone with rounded white chalk, subangular flint, and occasional well rounded brown quartzite and white quartz, and brownish black ironstone		
	Sand: medium and coarse with fine, mainly chalk, flint and quartz with a trace of glauconite; greyish brown		
Lower Chalk	Silt, dense becoming hard (siltstone), chalky and glauconitic, mottled pale yellow, light green	0.3+	5.7

GRADING

Mean for deposit *percentages*			Depth below surface (m)	*percentages*						
Fines	Sand	Gravel		Fines	Sand			Gravel		
				$-\frac{1}{16}$	$+\frac{1}{16}-\frac{1}{4}$	$+\frac{1}{4}-1$	$+1-4$	$+4-16$	$+16-64$	$+64$
19	41	40	1.1–2.3	19	10	19	12	26	14	0
			2.3–3.3	18	19	13	12	24	14	0
			3.3–4.3	16	11	19	11	27	16	0
			4.3–5.4	21	3	16	16	30	14	0
			Mean	19	11	17	13	26	14	0

COMPOSITION

Depth below surface (m)	Percentages (in +4−16 mm fraction)					
	Flint	Quartz and quartzite	Limestone	Chalk	Ironstone	Minor constituents
1.1−2.3	13	—	55	25	4	3
2.3−3.3	26	3	40	23	6	2
3.3−4.3	14	8	54	12	11	1
4.3−5.4	9	7	60	14	9	1
Mean	15	5	52	18	8	2

Surface level (c + 48.5 m) c + 159 ft   Overburden 0.7 m
Water level not recorded   Mineral 7.5 m
Percussion and core drilling   Bedrock 32.0 m +
March 1974

LOG

Geological classification	Lithology	Thickness m	Depth m
	Soil, clay with pebbles; dark brown	0.2	0.2
Made ground	Clay with weathered chalk; white	0.5	0.7

River Terrace Deposits (First Terrace)	Sand and gravel
	    Gravel: fine to cobble-size (maximum 100 mm diameter), predominantly limestone with quartz and quartzite
	    Sand: coarse, brown to yellow
		7.5	8.2

Lower Chalk	Chalk, hard, slightly micaceous and glauconitic with some minute shell fragments and some crushed sponges; yellowish grey	2.8	11.0
Upper Greensand	Siltstone, fine-grained, micaceous, sandy, calcitic, glauconitic with occasional sponge and shell fragments, and pyritised burrows; light greenish grey	29.2+	40.2

Surface level (c + 53.6 m) c + 176 ft   Overburden 0.5 m
Water not struck   Mineral 2.8 m
Shell and auger, 8 in (203 mm) diameter   Bedrock 0.7 m +
September 1975

LOG

Geological classification	Lithology	Thickness m	Depth m
	Soil, clayey with occasional quartz and flint pebbles, becoming more gravelly with depth; brown	0.5	0.5
River Terrace Deposits (Second Terrace)	'Clayey' sandy gravel Gravel: fine with some coarse, mainly buff rounded limestone with subangular to subrounded flint, occasional well rounded white quartz and well rounded brown quartzite, well rounded white chalk and reddish brown ironstone. Coarse fraction comprises mainly flint and quartzite Sand: medium with fine and coarse, comprises mainly quartz, flint and some ironstone and glauconite; light brown becoming rusty brown towards base	2.8	3.3
Upper Greensand	Sand, clayey; grey to greenish grey	0.7+	4.0

GRADING

Mean for deposit percentages			Depth below surface (m)	percentages						
Fines	Sand	Gravel		Fines	Sand			Gravel		
				$-\frac{1}{16}$	$+\frac{1}{16}-\frac{1}{4}$	$+\frac{1}{4}-1$	$+1-4$	$+4-16$	$+16-64$	$+64$
11	64	25	0.5–1.5	15	13	29	15	25	3	0
			1.5–2.5	6	21	34	18	16	5	0
			2.5–3.0	15	13	30	18	16	8	0
			3.0–3.3	12	8	29	17	26	8	0
			Mean	11	15	32	17	20	5	0

COMPOSITION

Depth below surface (m)	Percentages (in +4−16 mm fraction)					
	Flint	Quartz and quartzite	Limestone	Chalk	Ironstone	Minor constituents
0.5−1.5	28	6	45	6	14	1
1.5−2.5	13	5	62	7	12	1
2.5−3.0	14	12	50	16	8	—
3.0−3.3	10	15	66	3	6	—
Mean	18	8	54	8	11	1
	Percentages (in +16 mm fraction)					
0.5−1.5	73	—	23	—	4	—
1.5−2.5	35	56	—	9	—	—
2.5−3.0	21	66	11	2	—	—
3.0−3.3	31	33	32	1	1	2
Mean	46	35	14	4	1	tr

SU 58 NE 18   5853 8639   **West End, Cholsey**   **Block A**

Surface level (+47.9 m) +157 ft   Overburden 2.8 m
Water struck at (+45.5 m)   Mineral 5.8 m
Shell and auger, 8 in (203 mm) diameter   Bedrock 0.4 m +
September 1975

LOG

Geological classification	Lithology	Thickness m	Depth m
Made ground	Clay and soil with chalk pellets and black carbonaceous patches; black	0.4	0.4
	Clay, chalky and silty with some sand and flint gravel; chalk, white to greyish white	2.4	2.8

River Terrace Deposits (First Terrace)	Sandy gravel, becoming progressively more gravelly with depth
	    Gravel: fine to coarse with occasional cobbles (of quartz or quartzite), mainly well rounded buff to brown limestone with subangular to subrounded flint, well rounded white quartz, well rounded brown and reddish brown quartzite, well rounded chalk pellets and black ironstone; occasional greyish green marly siltstone
	    Sand: fine to coarse, mainly quartz, limestone and chalk with some ironstone and brown iron staining; reddish brown between 2.8 and 5.7 m, greyish white between 5.7 and 8.6 m
		5.8	8.6

Lower Chalk	Siltstone, marly, tabular and platy, glauconitic, greenish grey	0.4+	9.0

GRADING

Mean for deposit *percentages*			Depth below surface (m)	*percentages*						
Fines	Sand	Gravel		Fines	Sand			Gravel		
				$-\frac{1}{16}$	$+\frac{1}{16}-\frac{1}{4}$	$+\frac{1}{4}-1$	$+1-4$	$+4-16$	$+16-64$	$+64$
4	58	38	*2.8–3.9	9	53	20	5	13	0	0
			*3.9–5.0	3	12	34	12	38	1	0
			*5.0–5.7	4	16	33	19	24	4	0
			*5.7–6.7	4	7	31	24	30	4	0
			*6.7–8.2	2	4	19	21	41	13	0
			*8.2–8.6	4	6	13	18	33	26	0
			Mean	4	17	25	16	31	7	0

COMPOSITION

Depth below surface (m)	Percentages (in +4 − 16 mm fraction)					
	Flint	Quartz and quartzite	Limestone	Chalk	Ironstone	Minor constituents
2.8–3.9	22	2	49	26	1	—
3.9–5.0	9	7	62	0	22	—
5.0–5.7	17	7	56	4	16	—
5.7–6.7	11	8	68	3	9	1
6.7–8.2	8	8	67	3	14	—
8.2–8.6	4	3	85	—	8	—
Mean	12	6	64	6	12	tr
	Percentages (in +16 mm fraction)					
2.8–3.9	—	—	100	—	—	—
3.9–5.0	56	—	44	—	—	—
5.0–5.7	73	24	3	—	—	—
5.7–6.7	19	15	35	—	—	31
6.7–8.2	33	24	42	—	1	—
8.2–8.6	9	9	81	—	1	—
Mean	33	12	51	—	tr	4

Surface level (c + 48.8 m) c + 160 ft   Overburden 0.3 m
Water not struck   Mineral 3.0 m
Shell and auger, 8 in (203 mm) diameter   Bedrock 0.7 m +
September 1975

LOG

Geological classification	Lithology	Thickness m	Depth m
	Soil, sandy clay with occasional coarse angular flints; dark brown	0.3	0.3
River Terrace Deposits (Second Terrace)	'Clayey' sandy gravel Gravel: fine with some coarse, angular to subangular black flint, well rounded greyish brown limestone, well rounded white quartz and brown quartzite, blackish brown ironstone and chalk pellets, occasional siltstone Sand: medium with fine and coarse, mainly chalk and quartz; trace of glauconite; greyish white	3.0	3.3
Lower Chalk	Sand, chalky and silty, some glauconite; greenish grey	0.7 +	4.0

GRADING

Mean for deposit *percentages*			Depth below surface (m)	*percentages*						
Fines	Sand	Gravel		Fines	Sand			Gravel		
				$-\frac{1}{16}$	$+\frac{1}{16}-\frac{1}{4}$	$+\frac{1}{4}-1$	$+1-4$	$+4-16$	$+16-64$	$+64$
15	58	27	0.3–0.8	29	26	19	8	11	7	0
			0.8–1.8	17	11	20	16	28	8	0
			1.8–2.8	6	13	35	21	23	2	0
			2.8–3.3	17	13	32	15	18	5	0
			Mean	15	15	27	16	22	5	0

COMPOSITION

Depth below surface (m)	Percentages (in +4 – 16 mm fraction)					
	Flint	Quartz and quartzite	Limestone	Chalk	Ironstone	Minor constituents
0.3 – 0.8	49	27	5	7	11	1
0.8 – 1.8	19	56	—	15	10	—
1.8 – 2.8	27	7	49	6	11	—
2.8 – 3.3	10	8	43	35	4	—
Mean	25	27	24	14	10	tr
	Percentages (in +16 mm fraction)					
0.3–0.8	44	56	—	—	—	—
0.8–1.8	64	33	—	3	—	—
1.8–2.8	No coarse	—	—	—	—	—
2.8–3.3	81	10	9	—	—	—
Mean	63	33	2	2	—	—

Surface level (+48.8 m) +160 ft   Overburden 0.4 m
Water not struck   Mineral 1.6 m
Hand auger, 6 in (152 mm) diameter   Bedrock 2.1 m +
September 1975

LOG

Geological classification	Lithology	Thickness m	Depth m
	Soil, clayey with occasional well rounded white quartz, reddish brown quartzite, and flint; dark brown	0.4	0.4
River Terrace Deposits (Second Terrace)	'Very clayey' sandy gravel	1.6	2.0
	Gravel: fine with coarse, dominantly well rounded brown limestone, with subangular flint and black ironstone; occasional well rounded brown quartzite, well rounded white quartz and chalk; trace of green siltstone, flint with quartz and quartzite dominant constituents in coarse fractions(+16 mm)		
	Sand: medium with coarse and some fine quartz with chalk and glauconite; brown becoming light brown		
Lower Chalk	Clay, very chalky and silty with some glauconite and occasional reddish brown iron staining; soft becoming hard; whitish grey	2.1+	4.1

GRADING

Mean for deposit *percentages*			Depth below surface (m)	*percentages*						
Fines	Sand	Gravel		Fines	Sand			Gravel		
				$-\frac{1}{16}$	$+\frac{1}{16}-\frac{1}{4}$	$+\frac{1}{4}-1$	$+1-4$	$+4-16$	$+16-64$	$+64$
21	52	27	0.4–1.4	23	11	25	15	22	4	0
			1.4–2.0	18	8	25	21	19	9	0
			Mean	21	10	25	17	21	6	0

COMPOSITION

Depth below surface (m)	Percentages (in +4−16 mm fraction)					
	Flint	Quartz and quartzite	Limestone	Chalk	Ironstone	Minor constituents
0.4–1.4	19	4	60	—	17	—
1.4–2.0	16	10	51	7	15	1
Mean	18	6	56	3	16	1
	Percentages (in +16 mm fraction)					
0.4–1.4	44	56	—	—	—	—
1.4–2.0	63	28	3	—	—	6
Mean	54	42	1	—	—	3

Surface level (+45.4 m) +149 ft
Water struck at (+42.5 m)
Shell and auger, 6 in (152 mm) diameter
September 1975

Overburden 1.7 m
Mineral 2.1 m
Bedrock 1.7 m +

LOG

Geological classification	Lithology	Thickness m	Depth m
	Soil, light brown	0.4	0.4
River Terrace Deposits (First Terrace)	Clay, sandy with occasional fine to medium quartz and flint pebble; brown	1.3	1.7

	'Very clayey' sandy gravel with upper 1.2 m particularly clayey
	    Gravel: fine with occasional coarse, mainly rounded light brown limestone with angular to subrounded flint, occasional rounded quartz and quartzite, dark brown ironstone and chalk
	    Sand: medium with fine and coarse, mainly quartz and flint; buff to white
		2.1	3.8

Lower Chalk	Siltstone, chalky, friable becoming hard and compact with depth; greyish white	1.7+	5.5

GRADING

Mean for deposit *percentages*			Depth below surface (m)	*percentages*						
Fines	Sand	Gravel		Fines	Sand			Gravel		
				$-\frac{1}{16}$	$+\frac{1}{16}-\frac{1}{4}$	$+\frac{1}{4}-1$	$+1-4$	$+4-16$	$+16-64$	$+64$
26	41	33	1.7–2.9	43	5	33	1	16	2	0
			*2.9–3.8	3	9	20	15	37	16	0
			Mean	26	7	27	7	25	8	0

COMPOSITION

Depth below surface (m)	Percentages (in +4−16 mm fraction)					
	Flint	Quartz and quartzite	Limestone	Chalk	Ironstone	Minor constituents
1.7–2.9	6	3	78	4	9	—
2.9–3.8	27	5	57	5	6	—
Mean	20	4	64	5	7	—

Surface level (+43.3 m) +142 ft
Water struck at (+40.6 m)
Shell and auger, 6 in (152 mm) diameter
August 1972

Overburden 2.7 m
Mineral 2.3 m
Bedrock 0.3 m +

LOG

Geological classification	Lithology	Thickness m	Depth m
	Soil; dark brown	0.1	0.1
Alluvium	Clay, silty, soft with occasional carbonaceous streaks and small white gastropod shells; grey becoming brown	2.6	2.7
River Terrace Deposits (First Terrace)	Gravel	2.3	5.0
	Gravel: fine to coarse, mainly subrounded, tabular to platy, oolitic and shelly oolitic limestone with subangular to subrounded flint, light grey subangular to subrounded tabular chalk, brown ironstone and rounded white quartz and reddish brown quartzite; occasional worn shell fragments		
	Sand: medium and coarse with some fine, mainly flint quartz with ironstone and a little shell debris; brown		
Lower Chalk	Chalk, soft and silty, passing into firm and blocky chalk; light greenish grey	0.3 +	5.3

GRADING

Mean for deposit _percentages_			Depth below surface (m)	_percentages_						
Fines	Sand	Gravel		Fines	Sand				Gravel		
					$-\frac{1}{16}$	$+\frac{1}{16}-\frac{1}{4}$	$+\frac{1}{4}-1$	$+1-4$	$+4-16$	$+16-64$	$+64$
6	34	60	*2.7–3.7	7	1	11	13	42	26	0
			*3.7–5.0	5	3	24	15	27	26	0
			Mean	6	2	18	14	34	26	0

COMPOSITION

Depth below surface (m)	Percentages (in +4−16 mm fraction)					
	Flint	Quartz and quartzite	Limestone	Chalk	Ironstone	Minor constituents
2.7–3.7	10	5	60	13	11	1
3.7–5.0	24	4	53	11	8	—
Mean	17	4	56	12	10	1

Surface level (+46.6 m) +153 ft   Overburden 0.2 m
Water struck at (+41.8)   Mineral 4.8 m
Shell and auger, 6 in (152 mm) diameter   Bedrock 0.3 m+
August 1972

LOG

Geological classification	Lithology	Thickness m	Depth m
	Soil, with many flints; brown	0.2	0.2

River Terrace Deposits (First Terrace)	'Very clayey' gravel
	    Gravel: fine to coarse with occasional cobble, mainly angular, subangular and subrounded black and white coated (patina) flint with soft white chalk pellets; occasional well rounded white quartz; trace of limestone and ironstone
	    Sand: medium and coarse with fine, mainly quartz, flint and chalk with some glauconite; brown
		4.8	5.0

Lower Chalk	Chalk; pale grey	0.3+	5.3

GRADING

Mean for deposit percentages			Depth below surface (m)	percentages						
Fines	Sand	Gravel		Fines	Sand				Gravel		
				$-\frac{1}{16}$	$+\frac{1}{16}-\frac{1}{4}$	$+\frac{1}{4}-1$	$+1-4$	$+4-16$	$+16-64$	$+64$
34	27	39	0.2–1.2	32	1	12	14	25	16	0
			1.2–2.2	40	2	15	7	20	16	0
			2.2–3.2	33	1	11	11	22	22	0
			3.2–4.2	34	2	11	11	22	20	0
			4.2–5.0	30	3	20	14	15	18	0
			Mean	34	2	14	11	21	18	0

COMPOSITION

Depth below surface (m)	Percentages (in +4−16 mm fraction)				
	Flint	Quartz and quartzite	Limestone	Chalk	Ironstone
0.2–1.2	79	4	—	17	—
1.2–2.2	78	5	—	17	—
2.2–3.2	75	4	—	21	—
3.2–4.2	74	3	—	23	—
4.2–5.0	51	3	10	32	4
Mean	73	4	1	21	1

Surface level (c + 42.7 m) c + 140 ft   Overburden 1.8 m
Water struck at (c. + 40.9 m)   Mineral 3.1 m
Shell and auger, 8 in (203 mm) diameter   Bedrock 0.6 m +
September 1975

LOG

Geological classification	Lithology	Thickness m	Depth m
	Soil, clayey and silty; black	0.2	0.2
Alluvium	Clay, silty and soft, faintly mottled in grey; brown	1.6	1.8
River Terrace Deposits (First Terrace)	Gravel, becoming sandier with depth	3.1	4.9
	Gravel: fine to coarse with cobbles (mainly flint), mainly well rounded buff to brown limestone, with subangular to subrounded black and white coated (patina) flint, soft white chalk pellets and brownish black ironstone, occasional well rounded white quartz, and reddish brown quartzite. Flint predominates in the coarse fraction (+ 16 mm)		
	Sand: medium and coarse with some fine, mainly quartz, flint and chalk; chalk content increases with depth; light brown		
Middle Chalk	Chalk, soft with occasional flint; white	0.6 +	5.5

GRADING

Mean for deposit percentages			Depth below surface (m)	percentages							
Fines	Sand	Gravel		Fines	Sand				Gravel		
				$-\frac{1}{16}$	$+\frac{1}{16}-\frac{1}{4}$	$+\frac{1}{4}-1$	$+1-4$	$+4-16$	$+16-64$	$+64$
2	44	54	*1.8–2.8	3	1	13	19	32	26	6
			*2.8–3.8	1	3	19	19	30	28	0
			*3.8–4.9	2	6	27	25	29	10	1
			Mean	2	3	20	21	31	21	2

COMPOSITION

Depth below surface (m)	Percentages (in +4 – 16 mm fraction)				
	Flint	Quartz and quartzite	Limestone	Chalk	Ironstone
1.8–2.8	8	8	63	3	18
2.8–3.8	20	6	52	6	16
3.8–4.9	22	4	43	25	6
Mean	17	6	52	12	13
	Percentages (in + 16 mm fraction)				
1.8–2.8	69	21	9	—	1
2.8–3.8	68	29	2	1	—
3.8–4.9	70	—	—	30	—
Mean	69	16	4	11	tr

Surface level (c + 92.4 m) c + 303 ft   Overburden 0.1 m
Water not struck   Mineral 2.4 m +
Trench section
August 1976

LOG

Geological classification	Lithology	Thickness m	Depth m
	Soil, clayey and pebbly; brown	0.1	0.1
River Terrace Deposits (Fifth Terrace)	'Clayey' gravel Gravel: fine to coarse with cobbles, rounded to subangular grey and white coated flint, well rounded white quartz and well rounded red, reddish brown and black quartzite and Bunter sandstone; some rounded to tabular brownish black ironstone; rare sarsen boulder Sand: fine and medium with coarse, mainly quartz with flint; brown	2.4 +	2.5

GRADING

Mean for deposit _percentages_			Depth below surface (m)	_percentages_							
Fines	Sand	Gravel		Fines	Sand				Gravel		
				$-\frac{1}{16}$	$+\frac{1}{16}-\frac{1}{4}$	$+\frac{1}{4}-1$	$+1-4$	$+4-16$	$+16-64$	$+64$	
15	36	49	0.1–2.5	15	10	19	7	20	29	0	

COMPOSITION

Depth below surface (m)	Percentages (in +4−16 mm fraction)				
	Flint	Quartz	Quartzite (including Bunter Sandstone)	Limestone and chalk	Ironstone
0.1–2.5 +	52	26 19 45		tr	3
	Percentages (in −16 mm fraction)				
0.1–2.5 +	41	8 37 45		—	14

Surface level (+47.5 m) +156 ft   Overburden 1.0 m
Water struck at (+44.8 m)   Mineral 4.0 m
Shell and auger, 6 in (152 mm) diameter   Bedrock 0.5 m+
December 1971

LOG

Geological classification	Lithology	Thickness m	Depth m
	Soil, clayey with occasional flint and quartzite pebbles; dark brown	0.3	0.3
River Terrace Deposits (First Terrace)	Clay, sandy with occasional flint and quartzite pebbles, light brown	0.7	1.0
	Sandy gravel Gravel: fine with coarse, mainly subrounded brown limestone with subangular to subrounded flint, brownish black ironstone, and occasional well rounded brown quartzite with a trace of rounded quartz, rare green siltstone Sand: predominantly medium with some coarse and occasional fine, mainly quartz and limestone with some chalk; brown	4.0	5.0
Lower Chalk (Glauconitic Marl)	Siltstone, soft becoming very hard; chalky and glauconitic, light green	0.5+	5.5

GRADING

Mean for deposit *percentages*			Depth below surface (m)	*percentages*						
Fines	Sand	Gravel		Fines	Sand				Gravel		
				$-\frac{1}{16}$	$+\frac{1}{16}-\frac{1}{4}$	$+\frac{1}{4}-1$	$+1-4$	$+4-16$	$+16-64$	$+64$
7	67	28	1.0–1.6	8	5	80	2	4	1	0
			1.6–3.3	7	8	40	13	24	8	0
			*3.3–4.3	2	5	31	29	25	8	0
			*4.3–5.0	10	4	37	22	13	14	0
			Mean	6	6	44	17	19	8	0

COMPOSITION

Depth below surface (m)	Percentages (in +4−16 mm fraction)			
	Flint	Quartz and quartzite	Limestone and chalk	Ironstone
1.0–1.6	21	5	69	5
1.6–3.3	19	3	71	7
3.3–4.3	7	4	71	18
4.3–5.0	12	11	69	8
Mean	13	5	70	12

Surface level (+45.7 m) +150 ft   Overburden 1.2 m
Water struck at (+42.9)   Mineral 2.6 m
Shell and auger, 6 in (152 mm) diameter   Bedrock 1.0 m+
December 1971

LOG

Geological classification	Lithology	Thickness m	Depth m
	Soil, dark brown	0.2	0.2
River Terrace Deposits (First Terrace)	Clay, sandy with occasional subangular to subrounded flint, subrounded reddish brown quartzite, subrounded brown sandstone and light green siltstone; orange-brown	1.0	1.2
	'Clayey' pebbly sand	2.6	3.8
	Gravel: fine with occasional coarse, dominantly subrounded brown and light grey limestone, with subrounded brown ironstone, subangular to subrounded flint, and occasional reddish brown rounded quartzite and light green siltstone		
	Sand: dominantly medium with fine and some coarse, mainly quartz with some limestone, flint and glauconite; brown		
Lower Chalk	Siltstone, chalky with some glauconite, soft becoming dense and hard; pale green	1.0+	4.8

GRADING

Mean for deposit percentages			Depth below surface (m)	percentages						
Fines	Sand	Gravel		Fines	Sand			Gravel		
				$-\frac{1}{16}$	$+\frac{1}{16}-\frac{1}{4}$	$+\frac{1}{4}-1$	$+1-4$	$+4-16$	$+16-64$	$+64$
10	73	17	1.2–2.2	8	18	48	13	12	1	0
			2.2–3.2	15	24	51	4	5	1	0
			*3.2–3.8	4	6	41	14	27	8	0
			Mean	10	18	46	10	13	3	0

COMPOSITION

Depth below surface (m)	Percentages (in +4−16 mm fraction)				
	Flint	Quartz and quartzite	Limestone and chalk	Ironstone	Minor constituents
1.2–2.2	11	5	70	13	1
2.2–3.2	9	6	67	15	3
3.2–3.8	7	4	66	23	—
Mean	9	5	68	17	1

Surface level (+43.3 m) 142 ft
Water struck at (+41.0 m)
Shell and auger, 6 in (152 mm) diameter
December 1971

Overburden 3.4 m
Mineral 3.1 m
Bedrock 0.2 m+

LOG

Geological classification	Lithology	Thickness m	Depth m
	Soil; dark brown	0.1	0.1
Alluvium	Clay, silty, soft, with occasional shell, mottled orange-brown; brown becoming greyish blue	2.1	2.2
	Silt, clayey, soft, sandy peat at base with occasional shells; light brown and pale green becoming dark brown	1.2	3.4
River Terrace Deposits (First Terrace)	Gravel	3.1	6.5
	Gravel: fine with occasional coarse, dominantly subrounded to rounded, platy and tabular, brown and buff limestone, with some subrounded brown ironstone and occasional well rounded reddish brown quartzite, well rounded quartz and subangular flint		
	Sand: coarse with medium and occasional fine, mainly limestone and quartz; brown		
Lower Chalk	Siltstone, soft, becoming dense and hard, chalky and slightly glauconitic, some ironstaining in parts; light green	0.2+	6.7

GRADING

Mean for deposit *percentages*			Depth below surface (m)	*percentages*						
Fines	Sand	Gravel		Fines	Sand			Gravel		
				$-\frac{1}{16}$	$+\frac{1}{16}-\frac{1}{4}$	$+\frac{1}{4}-1$	$+1-4$	$+4-16$	$+16-64$	$+64$
2	42	56	*3.4–4.4	0	3	12	26	54	5	0
			*4.4–5.4	2	1	9	32	49	7	0
			*5.4–6.5	3	2	12	30	39	14	0
			Mean	2	2	11	29	47	9	0

COMPOSITION

Depth below surface (m)	Percentages (in +4−16 mm fraction)			
	Flint	Quartz and quartzite	Limestone and chalk	Ironstone
3.4–4.4	6	7	83	4
4.4–5.4	6	7	73	14
5.4–6.5	6	7	69	18
Mean	6	7	75	12

Surface level (+43.9 m) +144 ft   Overburden 1.6 m
Water struck at (+42.2)   Mineral 2.0 m
Shell and auger, 6 in (152 mm) diameter   Bedrock 0.5 m +
December 1971

LOG

Geological classification	Lithology	Thickness m	Depth m
	Soil, dark brown	0.1	0.1
Alluvium	Clay, silty, soft with occasional fine white shells, mottled greyish green; brown	1.3	1.4
	Silt and peat, clayey with occasional pebbles; grey to dark brown	0.2	1.6
River Terrace Deposits (First Terrace)	Gravel	2.0	3.6
	Gravel: fine to coarse with occasional cobbles, mainly subrounded brown limestone with rounded brownish black ironstone, subangular flint and occasional well rounded quartz and green siltstone; rare belemnites		
	Sand: medium and coarse with occasional fine, mainly quartz; brown		
Lower Chalk (Glauconitic Marl)	Siltstone, soft becoming hard, chalky with glauconitic; greyish green	0.5+	4.1

GRADING

Mean for deposit *percentages*			Depth below surface (m)	*percentages*						
Fines	Sand	Gravel		Fines	Sand			Gravel		
				$-\frac{1}{16}$	$+\frac{1}{16}-\frac{1}{4}$	$+\frac{1}{4}-1$	$+1-4$	$+4-16$	$+16-64$	$+64$
3	35	62	*1.6–2.6	2	2	17	15	33	31	0
			*2.6–3.6	3	3	18	17	38	21	0
			Mean	3	3	18	16	34	26	0

COMPOSITION

Depth below surface (m)	Percentages (in +4−16 mm fraction)			
	Flint	Quartz and quartzite	Limestone and chalk	Ironstone
1.6–2.6	8	6	55	31
2.6–3.6	9	4	70	17
Mean	9	5	64	22

Surface level (+45.4 m) +149 ft
Water struck at (+43.4 m)
Shell and auger, 6 in (152 mm) diameter
December 1971

Overburden 1.4 m
Mineral 4.4 m
Bedrock 0.6 m +

LOG

Geological classification	Lithology	Thickness m	Depth m
	Soil; dark brown	0.2	0.2
River Terrace Deposits (First Terrace)	Clay, sandy and silty, with occasional fine pebbles of chalk and flint; greyish brown	1.2	1.4

	Sandy gravel, with gravel increasing with depth
	  Gravel: fine with some coarse and rare cobbles, dominantly rounded oolitic limestone with angular to subangular flint, rounded brown ironstone and occasional rounded quartz and light green siltstone fragments
	  Sand: medium with coarse and occasional fine, mainly quartz with some flint and chalk; brown
		4.4	5.8

Lower Chalk	Siltstone, soft becoming hard, chalky with some glauconite; greyish green	0.6+	6.4

GRADING

Mean for deposit *percentages*			Depth below surface (m)	*percentages*						
Fines	Sand	Gravel		Fines	Sand			Gravel		
				$-\frac{1}{16}$	$+\frac{1}{16}-\frac{1}{4}$	$+\frac{1}{4}-1$	$+1-4$	$+4-16$	$+16-64$	$+64$
7	67	26	1.4–2.4	12	11	55	13	9	0	0
			*2.4–3.4	2	38	19	18	21	2	0
			*3.4–4.4	3	5	39	20	29	4	0
			*4.4–5.8	11	4	28	23	26	8	0
			Mean	7	9	39	19	22	4	0

COMPOSITION

Depth below surface (m)	Percentages (in +4−16 mm fraction)				
	Flint	Quartz and quartzite	Limestone and chalk	Ironstone	Minor constituents
1.4–2.4	12	3	74	7	4
2.4–3.4	13	5	72	10	—
3.4–4.4	11	6	72	11	—
4.4–5.8	13	4	69	14	—
Mean	12	4	71	12	1

Surface level (+49.7 m) +163 ft   Overburden 0.8 m
Water not struck   Mineral 2.3 m
Shell and auger, 6 in (152 mm) diameter   Bedrock 1.3 m +
December 1971

LOG

Geological classification	Lithology	Thickness m	Depth m
	Soil, dark brown	0.2	0.2
	Subsoil, brown	0.6	0.8
River Terrace Deposits (First Terrace)	'Clayey' gravel Gravel: fine to coarse with occasional cobble, mainly angular to subangular flint with subrounded brown limestone and occasional rounded black ironstone, well rounded quartz and well rounded chalk Sand: mainly medium with coarse and fine, predominantly quartz with occasional flint and chalk; brown	2.3	3.1
Lower Chalk	Siltstone, soft becoming hard, chalky and glauconitic with occasional flint pebbles; greyish green	1.3+	4.4

GRADING

Mean for deposit *percentages*			Depth below surface (m)	*percentages*						
Fines	Sand	Gravel		Fines	Sand			Gravel		
				$-\frac{1}{16}$	$+\frac{1}{16}-\frac{1}{4}$	$+\frac{1}{4}-1$	$+1-4$	$+4-16$	$+16-64$	$+64$
14	34	52	0.8–1.8	13	7	18	6	15	41	0
			1.8–3.1	14	8	21	9	22	26	0
			Mean	14	7	20	7	19	33	0

COMPOSITION

Depth below surface (m)	Percentages (in +4−16 mm fraction)			
	Flint	Quartz and quartzite	Limestone and chalk	Ironstone
0.8–1.8	50	3	45	2
1.8–3.1	69	—	25	6
Mean	62	1	32	5

Surface level (+ 106.1 m) +348 ft   Waste 1.9 m
Water not struck   Bedrock 0.5 m +
Shell and auger, 6 in (152 mm) diameter
September 1972

LOG

Geological classification	Lithology	Thickness m	Depth m
	Soil, clay with occasional pebbles; brown	0.3	0.3
Wallingford Fan Gravel	Clay, with gravel and sand; brown	1.6	1.9
	Gravel: fine to coarse with cobbles, predominantly angular to subangular flint with occasional well rounded quartz and quartzite, and brownish black ironstone		
	Sand: medium with coarse and fine, mainly quartz with flint		
Middle Chalk	Chalk, soft, with flints; white	0.5+	2.4

GRADING

Mean for deposit _percentages_			Depth below surface (m)	_percentages_						
Fines	Sand	Gravel		Fines	Sand			Gravel		
				$-\frac{1}{16}$	$+\frac{1}{16}-\frac{1}{4}$	$+\frac{1}{4}-1$	$+1-4$	$+4-16$	$+16-64$	$+64$
45	28	27	0.3–1.9	45	4	18	6	16	11	—

COMPOSITION

Depth below surface (m)	Percentages (in +4−16 mm fraction)				
	Flint	Quartz and quartzite	Limestone and chalk	Ironstone	Others
0.3–1.9	91	2	—	7	—

Surface level (+99.4 m) +326 ft	Overburden 0.2 m
Water not struck	Mineral 5.6 m
Shell and auger, 6 in (152 mm) diameter	Bedrock 0.5 m +
September 1972	

LOG

Geological classification	Lithology	Thickness m	Depth m
	Soil, clayey with occasional flint pebbles	0.2	0.2
Wallingford Fan Gravel	'Very clayey' gravel, with a clay lens between 3.5 m and 4.5 m. Deposit becomes more sandy with depth Gravel: fine to coarse with some cobbles, predominantly angular to subangular flint, occasional well rounded white quartz, well rounded reddish brown quartzite and brownish black ironstone Sand: medium with some fine and occasional coarse, mainly quartz with flint; light brown	5.6	5.8
Middle Chalk	Chalk, soft, with occasional flint; white	0.5+	6.3

GRADING

Mean for deposit *percentages*			Depth below surface (m)	*percentages*						
Fines	Sand	Gravel		Fines	Sand			Gravel		
				$-\frac{1}{16}$	$+\frac{1}{16}-\frac{1}{4}$	$+\frac{1}{4}-1$	$+1-4$	$+4-16$	$+16-64$	$+64$
26	36	38	0.2–1.3	19	3	10	5	19	44	0
			1.3–2.5	21	5	24	6	20	24	0
			2.5–3.5	22	5	25	6	17	25	0
			3.5–4.5	50	2	14	6	16	12	0
			4.5–5.2	23	4	39	4	11	19	0
			5.2–5.8	21	17	60	0	1	1	0
			Mean	26	12	21	3	15	23	0

COMPOSITION

Depth below surface (m)	Percentages (in +4−16 mm fraction)			
	Flint	Quartz and quartzite	Limestone and chalk	Ironstone
0.2–1.3	84	8	—	8
1.3–2.5	84	9	—	7
2.5–3.5	89	6	—	5
3.5–4.5	89	4	—	7
4.5–5.2	70	18	—	12
5.2–5.8	68	20	—	12
Mean	80	11	—	9

Surface level (c + 45.7 m) c + 150 ft
Water struck at (c + 43.4 m)
Shell and auger, 8 in (203 mm) diameter
September 1975

LOG

Geological classification	Lithology	Thickness m	Depth m
	Soil, clayey with occasional fine limestone pebbles; blackish brown becoming brown	0.4	0.4
River Terrace Deposits (First Terrace)	Clay, sandy, becoming clayey and silty with depth, rare fine angular flint and limestone pebbles, mottled greenish brown to white; light brown	1.3	1.7
	'Clayey' gravel; clayey and sandy in upper 0.7 m; sand component decreases with depth	2.1	3.8
	Gravel: fine to coarse with occasional cobbles, mainly well rounded to rounded buff to brown limestone with subangular to angular brown and black flint, brownish black ironstone and occasional well rounded white quartz and well rounded reddish brown quartzite, and soft white chalk; rare greyish green glauconitic siltstone. Base of deposit comprises much coarse tabular and platy, greyish green siltstone. In the coarse fraction (+ 16 m) flint is the dominant constituent		
	Sand: medium with coarse and some fine, mainly quartz with limestone and flint, and some chalk; whitish grey		
Lower Chalk (Glauconitic Marl)	Siltstone, soft, silty and sandy becoming hard, chalky and glauconitic; reddish brown (iron oxide) speckles; light green becoming dark green	0.2+	4.0

GRADING

Mean for deposit *percentages*			Depth below surface (m)	*percentages*						
Fines	Sand	Gravel		Fines	Sand			Gravel		
				$-\frac{1}{16}$	$+\frac{1}{16}-\frac{1}{4}$	$+\frac{1}{4}-1$	$+1-4$	$+4-16$	$+16-64$	$+64$
11	40	49	1.7–2.4	23	14	29	8	19	7	0
			*2.4–3.0	3	5	17	17	33	25	0
			*3.0–3.8	7	6	13	13	34	27	0
			Mean	11	8	20	12	29	20	0

COMPOSITION

Depth below surface (m)	Percentages (in +4 – 16 mm fraction)					
	Flint	Quartz and quartzite	Limestone	Chalk	Ironstone	Minor constituents
1.7–2.4	24	9	52	4	11	—
2.4–3.0	17	1	65	3	14	—
3.0–3.8	15	4	65	3	13	—
Mean	18	5	61	3	13	—
	Percentages (in +16 mm fraction)					
1.7–2.4	75	6	19	tr	—	—
2.4–3.0	75	11	14	—	—	—
3.0–3.8	71	10	18	—	—	1
Mean	74	9	17	—	—	tr

Surface level (+49.4 m) +162 ft   Overburden 0.3 m
Water not struck   Mineral 3.8 m
Gravel pit exposure and hand auger 6 in (152 mm) diameter   Bedrock 0.2 m +
September 1975

LOG

Geological classification	Lithology	Thickness m	Depth m
	Soil and subsoil, sandy and clayey with numerous fine to coarse flint pebbles	0.3	0.3
River Terrace Deposits (First Terrace)	Gravel	3.8	4.1
	Gravel; fine to coarse with numerous cobbles, predominantly angular to subangular white-coated black, or brown flint with occasional brownish black ironstone, well rounded quartz, well rounded reddish brown or black quartzite, well rounded chalk; trace of greyish green platy to tabular siltstone becoming increasingly common towards the base. Coarse fraction (+16 mm) comprises almost entirely flint		
	Sand: medium with coarse and fine, mainly flint with quartz and some chalk; trace of ironstone; brownish white		
Lower Chalk	Chalk, soft; whitish grey	0.2+	4.3

GRADING

Mean for deposit *percentages*			Depth below surface (m)	*percentages*						
Fines	Sand	Gravel		Fines	Sand			Gravel		
				$-\frac{1}{16}$	$+\frac{1}{16}-\frac{1}{4}$	$+\frac{1}{4}-1$	$+1-4$	$+4-16$	$+16-64$	$+64$
6	31	63	0.3–1.2	6	6	13	3	10	53	9
			1.2–2.2	6	6	14	8	21	40	5
			2.2–3.2	5	11	17	11	20	36	0
			3.2–4.1	8	9	16	10	25	32	0
			Mean	6	8	15	8	19	41	3

COMPOSITION

Depth below surface (m)	Percentages (in +4 – 16 mm fraction)					
	Flint	Quartz and quartzite	Limestone	Chalk	Ironstone	Minor constituents
0.3–1.2	94	1	—	—	5	—
1.2–2.2	98	—	—	1	1	—
2.2–3.2	72	2	—	—	25	1
3.2–4.1	50	1	—	1	32	16
Mean	79	1	—	tr	16	4
	Percentages (in +16 mm fraction)					
0.3–1.2	99	—	—	1	—	—
1.2–2.2	100	—	—	—	—	—
2.2–3.2	100	—	—	—	—	—
3.2–4.1	100	—	—	—	—	—
Mean	100	—	—	tr	—	—

Surface level (+ 100.6 m) + 330 ft   Overburden 0.3 m
Water not struck   Mineral 5.2 m
Gravel pit exposure   Bedrock 0.2 m +
July 1975

LOG

Geological classification	Lithology	Thickness m	Depth m
	Soil, sandy and clayey with flints; brown	0.3	0.3
Wallingford Fan Gravel	'Clayey' gravel	5.2	5.5
	Gravel: fine to coarse with numerous cobbles, predominantly angular brown, black and white coated (patina) flint with occasional well rounded white quartz and brownish black ironstone, rare reddish brown sandstone, shell fragment, sarsen, puddingstone and chalk. Coarse fraction (16 mm +) almost entirely flint		
	Sand: fine to medium with coarse, mainly quartz and flint; brown		
Middle Chalk	Chalk, soft; white	0.2 +	5.7

GRADING

Mean for deposit percentages			Depth below surface (m)	percentages						
Fines	Sand	Gravel		Fines	Sand			Gravel		
				$-\frac{1}{16}$	$+\frac{1}{16}-\frac{1}{4}$	$+\frac{1}{4}-1$	$+1-4$	$+4-16$	$+16-64$	$+64$
12	26	62	0.3–1.3	9	11	6	5	39	30	0
			1.3–2.3	17	14	9	4	21	35	0
			2.3–3.3	9	10	13	6	17	45	0
			3.3–4.3	9	8	11	6	23	43	0
			4.3–5.5	12	16	9	2	16	45	0
			Mean	12	12	10	4	25	37	0

COMPOSITION

Depth below surface (m)	Percentages (in +4−16 mm fraction)				
	Flint	Quartz	Chalk	Ironstone	Minor constituents
0.3–1.3	48	31	1	1	19
1.3–2.3	96	2	—	2	—
2.3–3.3	84	3	—	5	8
3.3–4.3	94	1	—	5	—
4.3–5.5	85	—	9	6	—
Mean	82	7	2	4	5
	Percentages (in +16 mm fraction)				
0.3–1.3	97	—	—	—	3
1.3–2.3	100	—	—	—	—
2.3–3.3	100	—	—	—	—
3.3–4.3	100	—	—	—	—
4.3–5.5	98	—	1	1	—
Mean	99	—	tr	tr	1

Surface level (+ 101.5 m) +333 ft
Water not struck
Shell and auger 8 in (203 mm) diameter
September 1975

Overburden 3.7 m
Mineral 4.3 m
Bedrock 3.5 m +

LOG

Geological classification	Lithology	Thickness m	Depth m
	Soil, brown	0.3	0.3
Wallingford Fan Gravel	Clay, sandy with fine to cobble-size, angular to subrounded flint and occasional quartz and ironstone; reddish brown	3.4	3.7

	'Very clayey' gravel
	    Gravel: fine to coarse with cobbles, predominantly subangular to subrounded grey and white coated (patina) flint with occasional reddish brown ironstone and well rounded white quartz, rare red cherts and chalk pellets. Coarse fraction (16 mm +) consists entirely of flint.
	    Sand: fine to medium quartz and flint with coarse, clayey throughout; occasional oxide staining; reddish brown
		4.3	8.0

Middle Chalk	Chalk, soft; white	0.5+	8.5

GRADING

Mean for deposit percentages			Depth below surface (m)	percentages						
Fines	Sand	Gravel		Fines	Sand			Gravel		
				$-\frac{1}{16}$	$+\frac{1}{16}-\frac{1}{4}$	$+\frac{1}{4}-1$	$+1-4$	$+4-16$	$+16-64$	$+64$
36	21	43	3.7–5.0	43	13	8	3	7	24	2
			5.0–8.0	28	6	8	6	16	36	0
			Mean	33	8	8	5	13	32	1

COMPOSITION

Depth below surface (m)	Percentages (in +4−16 mm fraction)				
	Flint	Quartz	Chalk	Ironstone	Minor constituents
3.7–8.0	82	2	tr	15	1
	Percentages (in +16 mm fraction)				
3.7–8.0	100	—	—	—	—

Surface level (c + 98.8 m) c + 324 ft
Water not struck
Trench section
September 1976

Overburden 0.1 m
Mineral 3.0 m +

LOG

Geological classification	Lithology	Thickness m	Depth m
	Soil, clayey and sandy with numerous flint pebbles	0.1	0.1
Wallingford Fan Gravel	'Clayey' gravel, with stratified sand, and gravelly (mostly chalk) sand seams near the base of the deposit	3.0+	3.1
	Gravel: fine to coarse with cobbles, predominantly ill-sorted angular to subrounded grey, brown and white coated (patina) flint with occasional white chalk, rare well rounded white quartz and brown ironstone		
	Sand: fine with medium and rare coarse, clayey throughout, mainly quartz with flint, dark brown to brown, sand seams, light brown to white		

GRADING

Mean for deposit *percentages*			Depth below surface (m)	*percentages*						
Fines	Sand	Gravel		Fines	Sand			Gravel		
				$-\frac{1}{16}$	$+\frac{1}{16}-\frac{1}{4}$	$+\frac{1}{4}-1$	$+1-4$	$+4-16$	$+16-64$	$+64$
15	36	49	0.1–3.1	15	20	15	1	13	36	0

COMPOSITION

Depth below surface (m)	Percentages (in +4−16 mm fraction)			
	Flint	Quartz and quartzite	Limestone and chalk	Ironstone
0.1–3.1	100	—	tr	—

Depth below surface (m)	Percentages (in +16 mm fraction)			
0.1–3.1	100	tr	tr	tr

Surface level (+46.6 m) +153 ft   Overburden 1.3 m
Water not struck   Mineral 2.9 m
Shell and auger, 6 in (152 mm) diameter   Bedrock 1.0 m +
December 1971

LOG

Geological classification	Lithology	Thickness m	Depth m
	Soil; dark brown	0.2	0.2
Alluvium	Sand, clayey and silty with occasional flint pebbles; reddish brown	1.1	1.3
River Terrace Deposits (First Terrace)	'Very clayey' gravel Gravel: fine to coarse with occasional cobbles, well rounded chalk and angular to subangular flint, occasional well rounded white quartz and brownish black ironstone Sand: medium with coarse and fine, predominantly quartz with some flint and chalk; brown	2.9	4.2
Lower Chalk	Siltstone; soft becoming dense and hard, chalky and slightly glauconitic; greyish green	1.0+	5.2

GRADING

Mean for deposit *percentages*			Depth below surface (m)	*percentages*						
Fines	Sand	Gravel		Fines	Sand				Gravel		
				$-\frac{1}{16}$	$+\frac{1}{16}-\frac{1}{4}$	$+\frac{1}{4}-1$	$+1-4$	$+4-16$	$+16-64$	$+64$
23	38	39	1.3–2.3	35	4	22	7	18	14	0
			2.3–3.3	22	16	22	8	13	19	0
			3.3–4.2	13	4	18	13	21	31	0
			Mean	23	8	21	9	18	21	0

COMPOSITION

Depth below surface (m)	Percentages (in +4–16 mm fraction)			
	Flint	Quartz and quartzite	Chalk	Ironstone
1.3–2.3	18	3	74	5
2.3–3.3	48	—	44	8
3.3–4.2	64	5	28	3
Mean	46	3	46	5

Surface level (+55.8 m) +183 ft   Overburden 0.2 m
Water not struck   Mineral 4.8 m
Shell and auger, 6 in (152 mm) diameter   Bedrock 0.5 m+
September 1972

LOG

Geological classification	Lithology	Thickness m	Depth m
	Soil, clayey and sandy with occasional flint and quartzite pebbles; brown	0.2	0.2
Alluvium [River Terrace Deposits (First Terrace)]	'Very clayey' gravel Gravel: fine to coarse with many cobbles, ill-sorted, predominantly angular grey or white coated (patina) flint with some chalk, occasional well rounded quartz and quartzite and brown black ironstone Sand: coarse and medium with occasional fine; mainly quartz, flint and chalk; greyish white	4.8	5.0
Lower Chalk	Siltstone, soft becoming hard, sandy, chalky and glauconitic; light green	0.5+	5.5

GRADING

Mean for deposit *percentages*			Depth below surface (m)	*percentages*						
Fines	Sand	Gravel		Fines	Sand			Gravel		
				$-\frac{1}{16}$	$+\frac{1}{16}-\frac{1}{4}$	$+\frac{1}{4}-1$	$+1-4$	$+4-16$	$+16-64$	$+64$
22	32	46	0.2–1.3	21	0	19	4	17	39	0
			1.3–2.3	8	1	15	40	20	16	0
			2.3–3.3	25	3	16	6	16	34	0
			3.3–4.3	33	3	10	12	24	18	0
			4.3–5.0	22	2	15	13	25	23	0
			Mean	22	2	15	15	20	26	0

COMPOSITION

Depth below surface (m)	Percentages (in +4−16 mm fraction)				
	Flint	Quartz	Chalk	Ironstone	Minor constituents
0.2–1.3	91	2	3	2	2
1.3–2.3	71	2	23	4	—
2.3–3.3	70	—	26	4	—
3.3–4.3	81	—	16	3	—
4.3–5.0	82	1	14	3	—
Mean	80	1	15	3	1

Surface level (+ 112.8 m) + 370 ft   Overburden 0.4 m
Water not struck   Mineral 6.3 m
Shell and auger, 6 in (152 mm) diameter   Bedrock 1.5 m +
February 1972

LOG

Geological classification	Lithology	Thickness m	Depth m
	Soil	0.4	0.4
River Terrace Deposits (Seventh Terrace)	'Very clayey' sandy gravel, with the upper 0.8 m consisting of a low-fines sandy gravel horizon Gravel: fine with some coarse, predominantly subangular to subrounded flint, with occasional well rounded white quartz and brownish black ironstone Sand: medium with fine and coarse, mainly quartz and flint, clayey and silty throughout; brown	6.3	6.7
Upper Chalk	Chalk with coarse to cobble-size flints; white	1.5+	8.2

GRADING

Mean for deposit *percentages*			Depth below surface (m)	*percentages*						
Fines	Sand	Gravel		Fines	Sand			Gravel		
				$-\frac{1}{16}$	$+\frac{1}{16}-\frac{1}{4}$	$+\frac{1}{4}-1$	$+1-4$	$+4-16$	$+16$	$+64$
25	21	54	0.4–1.2	8	7	12	8	31	34	0
			1.2–2.3	28	3	5	6	24	34	0
			2.3–3.2	32	3	11	6	24	24	0
			3.2–4.2	34	1	4	6	15	40	0
			4.2–5.2	22	3	16	9	26	24	0
			5.2–6.7	25	4	15	9	27	20	0
			Mean	25	3	11	7	24	30	0

COMPOSITION

Depth below surface (m)	Percentages (in +4−16 mm fraction)				
	Flint	Quartz and quartzite	Limestone	Chalk	Ironstone
0.4–1.2	87	4	—	—	9
1.2–2.2	80	13	—	—	7
2.2–3.2	81	13	—	—	6
3.2–4.2	90	6	—	—	4
4.2–5.2	75	16	—	—	9
5.2–6.7	77	10	—	—	13
Mean	82	10	—	—	8

SU 68 SW 4   6377 8077   Cray's Pond, Goring Heath

Surface level (+116.1 m) +545 ft   Waste 2.2 m
Water not struck   Bedrock 11.0 m+
Shell and auger, 6 in (152 mm) diameter
December 1971

LOG

Geological classification	Lithology	Thickness m	Depth m
	Soil; brown	0.1	0.1
	Subsoil, weathered sandy clay becoming silty with depth; some fine to coarse, angular to subangular flint; occasional rounded chalk, rare rounded quartz; reddish brown	2.1	2.2
Reading Beds	Sand with a trace of gravel; gravel content increases noticeably from 9.2 to 12.2 m	11.0+	13.2
	Gravel; predominantly fine with occasional coarse and cobbles, angular to subangular flint, with occasional rounded quartz and reddish brown ironstone		
	Sand; medium with fine and rare coarse, rounded, predominantly quartzitic; orange-brown		

SU 68 SW 5   6255 8187   Beech Farm, Goring

Surface level (+135.9 m) +446 ft   Waste 3.7 m
Water not struck   Bedrock 0.5 m+
Shell and auger, 6 in (152 mm) diameter
July 1972

LOG

Geological classification	Lithology	Thickness m	Depth m
	Soil	0.3	0.3
Clay-with-flints	Clay, silty, with some flint pebbles; brown	3.4	3.7
Upper Chalk	Chalk with occasional flint; cream-white	0.5+	4.2

SU 68 SW 6   6350 8220   Broad Street Farm, Woodcote

Surface level (+151.2 m) +496 ft   Waste 2.1 m
Water not struck   Bedrock 0.5 m+
Shell and auger, 6 in (152 mm) diameter
July 1972

LOG

Geological classification	Lithology	Thickness m	Depth m
	Soil	0.1	0.1
Clay-with-flints	Clay, with fine to cobble-size, angular to subangular flints; traces of quartz and ironstone; some sand; reddish brown	2.0	2.1
Upper Chalk	Chalk with occasional flints; white	0.5+	2.6

SU 68 SW 7   6483 8272   North of Woodcote Farm, Woodcote   **Block D**

Surface level (+ 166.4 m) + 546 ft   Waste 11.8 m
Water not struck   Bedrock 0.5 m +
Shell and auger, 6 in (152 mm) diameter
July 1972

LOG

Geological classification	Lithology	Thickness m	Depth m
	Soil, brown	0.4	0.4
Sand and gravel of unknown origin	Clay, silty and sandy, with rounded quartz and fine to coarse flint with occasional ironstone; mottled grey to orange-brown becoming dark brown	5.7	6.1

Clay-with-flints	Clay, with flint gravel, and sand
	  Gravel: fine to coarse with cobbles, predominantly
	    angular to subrounded, black and white coated (patina)
	    flint and nodular flint cobbles with occasional well rounded
	    quartz and brownish black ironstone
	  Sand: fine and medium with coarse, mainly quartz
	  with flint clay: dark brown with black manganese (?)
	    staining near the base
		5.7	11.8

Upper Chalk	Chalk, soft with flints and brown clay seams; white	0.5 +	12.3

SU 68 SW 8   6452 8065   Friarhampstead Wood, Goring Heath

Surface level (+ 161.2 m) + 529 ft   Waste 1.4 m
Water not struck   Bedrock 0.6 m +
Shell and auger, 6 in (152 mm) diameter
July 1972

LOG

Geological classification	Lithology	Thickness m	Depth m
	Soil	0.2	0.2
Reading Beds	Clay, silty, with occasional flint pebbles; light orange-brown	1.2	1.4
Upper Chalk	Chalk with coarse to cobble-size angular to rounded flint; white	0.6 +	2.0

Surface level (c + 64.0 m) c + 210 ft
Water not struck
Shell and auger, 8 in (203 mm) diameter
September 1975

Overburden 0.2 m
Mineral 8.3 m
Bedrock 0.3 m +

LOG

Geological classification	Lithology	Thickness m	Depth m
	Soil, sandy with occasional flint and quartzite pebbles; brown	0.2	0.2
River Terrace Deposits (Third Terrace)	'Very clayey' pebbly sand, with silty and sandy clay lenses between 2.2 m and 3.2 m, and 4.6 m and 6.2 m	8.3	8.5
	Gravel: fine to coarse, subangular to subrounded flint, rounded chalk and rounded brownish white limestone with occasional brownish black ironstone, well rounded white quartz and well rounded reddish brown quartzite, rare tabular greyish green siltstone		
	Sand: fine and medium with coarse, mainly quartz with some flint; light brown		
Lower Chalk	Chalk, soft and pliable; greyish white	0.3 +	8.8

GRADING

Mean for deposit percentages			Depth below surface (m)	percentages							
Fines	Sand	Gravel		Fines	Sand				Gravel		
				$-\frac{1}{16}$	$+\frac{1}{16}-\frac{1}{4}$	$+\frac{1}{4}-1$	$+1-4$	$+4-16$	$+16-64$	$+64$	
31	53	16	0.2–1.2	29	32	21	2	7	9	0	
			1.2–2.2	22	37	17	5	11	8	0	
			.2–4.2	38	30	17	3	8	4	0	
			4.2–4.6	38	23	12	7	12	8	0	
			6.2–7.2	39	19	20	8	12	2	0	
			7.2–8.5	20	22	32	8	14	4	0	
			Mean	31	26	21	6	11	5	0	

COMPOSITION

Depth below surface (m)	Percentages (in +4−16 mm fraction)					
	Flint	Quartz and quartzite	Limestone	Chalk	Ironstone	Minor constituents
0.2–1.2	78	11	1	1	8	1
1.2–2.2	64	10	—	25	1	—
3.2–4.2	40	5	1	52	1	1
4.2–4.6	51	8	—	36	3	2
6.2–7.2	22	5	36	32	5	—
7.2–8.5	22	6	50	17	5	—
Mean	41	7	18	30	4	tr
	Percentages (in +16 mm fraction)					
0.2–1.2	94	6	—	—	—	—
1.2–2.2	100	—	—	—	—	—
.2–4.2	93	—	—	7	—	—
4.2–4.6	91	5	—	2	—	2
.2–7.2	77	15	—	8	—	—
7.2–8.5	67	—	27	—	6	—
Mean	85	5	5	4	1	tr

Surface level (c+82.6 m) c+271 ft
Water not struck
Shell and auger, 8 in (203 mm) diameter
September 1975

Overburden 0.1 m
Mineral 2.2 m
Bedrock 0.2 m+

LOG

Geological classification	Lithology	Thickness m	Depth m
	Soil, brown	0.1	0.1
Wallingford Fan Gravel	'Very clayey' sandy gravel	2.2	2.3
	Gravel: fine to coarse with cobbles, predominantly subangular to angular grey and black flint with occasional well rounded quartz and quartzite, brownish black ironstone and white chalk Sand: fine and medium with some coarse, mainly quartz with flint, very clayey throughout; dark brown		
Middle Chalk	Chalk, soft; white	0.2+	2.5

GRADING

Mean for deposit *percentages*			Depth below surface (m)	*percentages*						
Fines	Sand	Gravel		Fines	Sand			Gravel		
				$-\frac{1}{16}$	$+\frac{1}{16}-\frac{1}{4}$	$+\frac{1}{4}-1$	$+1-4$	$+4-16$	$+16-64$	$+64$
31	39	30	0.1–1.2	31	27	17	3	8	14	0
			1.2–2.3	30	11	14	6	15	24	0
			Mean	31	19	15	5	11	19	0

COMPOSITION

Depth below surface (m)	Percentages (in +4−16 mm fraction)			
	Flint	Quartz and quartzite	Chalk	Ironstone
0.1–1.2	92	3	—	5
1.2–2.3	84	2	5	9
Mean	88	3	2	7
	Percentages (in +16 mm fraction)			
0.1–1.2	95	5	—	—
1.2–2.3	98	—	2	—
Mean	96	3	1	—

Surface level (c + 111.2 m) c + 365 ft   Overburden 0.1 m
Water not struck   Mineral 1.5 m
Shell and auger, 8 in (203 mm) diameter   Bedrock 0.4 m +
September 1975

LOG

Geological classification	Lithology	Thickness m	Depth m
	Soil, sandy and clayey with numerous pebbles of flint, quartz and quartzite; brown	0.1	0.1
River Terrace Deposits (Seventh Terrace)	'Very clayey' gravel, clay content increases in lower 0.5 m	1.5	1.6
	Gravel: fine to coarse with cobbles, predominantly angular to subangular and occasionally subrounded flint with occasional well-rounded white quartz, brownish black ironstone, and white chalk; rare well-rounded quartzite		
	Sand: fine to coarse, mainly quartz with flint; brown		
Upper Chalk	Chalk, soft, with occasional flint; white	0.4+	2.0

GRADING

Mean for deposit *percentages*			Depth below surface (m)	*percentages*						
Fines	Sand	Gravel		Fines	Sand			Gravel		
				$-\frac{1}{16}$	$+\frac{1}{16}-\frac{1}{4}$	$+\frac{1}{4}-1$	$+1-4$	$+4-16$	$+16-64$	$+64$
22	26	52	0.1–1.6	22	8	9	9	20	32	0

COMPOSITION

Depth below surface (m)	Percentages (in +4−16 mm fraction)				
	Flint	Quartz and quartzite	Chalk	Ironstone	Minor constituents
0.1–1.6	80	4	8	7	1
	Percentages (in +16 mm fraction)				
0.1–1.6	89	8	3	—	—

SU 68 SE 1   6955 8235   Kingwood Common, Rotherfield Peppard

Surface level (+ 124.7 m) +409 ft   Waste 7.8 m
Water not struck   Bedrock 0.5 m +
Shell and auger, 6 in (152 mm) diameter
July 1972

LOG

Geological classification	Lithology	Thickness m	Depth m
Made ground	Clay, brown	0.4	0.4
Clay-with-flints	Clay; silty, mottled reddish brown, some black manganese staining, with fine to coarse angular flint; brown	7.4	7.8
Upper Chalk	Chalk, soft, with occasional flints; white	0.5+	8.3

SU 68 SE 2   6863 8208   Borocourt, Checkendon

Surface level (+ 127.7 m) +419 ft   Waste 6.6 m
Water not struck   Bedrock 0.5 m +
Shell and auger, 6 in (152 mm) diameter
July 1972

LOG

Geological classification	Lithology	Thickness m	Depth m
	Soil	0.1	0.1
(River Terrace Deposits ?)	Clay, sandy, with pebbles of flint and some rounded quartzite; brown	0.7	0.8
Clay-with-flints	Flints in silty clay, some black manganese staining; reddish brown	5.8	6.6
Upper Chalk	Chalk, with occasional flints, soft; cream-white	0.5+	7.1

Surface level (+140.8 m) +462 ft   Waste 6.3 m
Water not struck   Bedrock 0.5 m +
Shell and auger, 6 in (152 mm) diameter
July 1972

LOG

Geological classification	Lithology	Thickness m	Depth m
	Soil; brown	0.1	0.1

River Terrace Deposits (Eighth Terrace)	'Very clayey' gravel
	    Gravel: fine with coarse and occasional cobbles, subangular to subrounded flint, and rounded white quartz, occasional brownish black ironstone
	    Sand: fine to coarse, mainly quartz with flint; dark brown
		0.6	0.7

Clay-with-flints	Clay, with subangular to subrounded flints, well rounded quartz and occasional ironstone; mottled reddish brown with some dark brown (manganese ?) staining; brown	5.6	6.3
Upper Chalk	Chalk, soft with brown clay seams; white	0.5+	6.8

GRADING

Mean for deposit percentages			Depth below surface (m)	percentages						
Fines	Sand	Gravel		Fines	Sand			Gravel		
				$-\frac{1}{16}$	$+\frac{1}{16}-\frac{1}{4}$	$+\frac{1}{4}-1$	$+1-4$	$+4-16$	$+16-64$	$+64$
23	7	70	0.1–0.7	23	2	2	3	16	54	—

COMPOSITION

Depth below surface (m)	Percentages (in +4−16 mm fraction)			
	Flint	Quartz	Limestone and chalk	Ironstone
0.1–0.7	37	58	—	5

Surface level (+ 155.4 m) +510 ft
Water not struck
Shell and auger, 6 in (152 mm) diameter
July 1972

Overburden 7.3 m
Mineral 3.1 m
Waste 2.7 m
Bedrock 0.5 m +

LOG

Geological classification	Lithology	Thickness m	Depth m
	Soil, brown	0.2	0.2
River Terrace Deposits (Eighth Terrace)	Clay, sandy and silty, with occasional flint and quartz pebbles, mottled reddish brown and grey, some brown (manganese ?) staining; brown	7.1	7.3
	'Very clayey' gravel	3.1	10.4
	Gravel: fine to coarse, subangular to subrounded flint and rounded quartz and quartzite with occasional brownish black ironstone		
	Sand: medium and coarse with some fine, mainly quartz with flint; light brown becoming orange-brown		
Clay-with-flints	Clay; mildly sandy, some black (manganese ?) staining; dark brown, with fine to cobble-size, angular to subangular flint	2.7	13.1
Upper Chalk	Chalk, soft with occasional fine to coarse flints and brown clay seams; white	0.5+	13.6

GRADING

Mean for deposit *percentages*			Depth below surface (m)	*percentages*						
Fines	Sand	Gravel		Fines	Sand				Gravel	
				$-\frac{1}{16}$	$+\frac{1}{16}-\frac{1}{4}$	$+\frac{1}{4}-1$	$+1-4$	$+4-16$	$+16-64$	$+64$
26	25	49	7.3–8.3	24	1	13	15	24	23	0
			8.3–9.3	23	4	11	10	28	24	0
			9.3–10.4	31	2	11	9	22	25	0
			Mean	26	2	12	11	25	24	0

COMPOSITION

Depth below surface (m)	Percentages (in +4−16 mm fraction)					
	Flint	Quartz and quartzite	Limestone	Chalk	Ironstone	Minor constituents
7.3–8.3	11	84	—	—	5	—
8.3–9.3	44	54	-	—	2	—
9.3–10.4	39	54	—	—	1	6
Mean	31	64	—	—	3	2

Surface level (+137.5 m) +451 ft   Waste 2.6 m
Water not struck   Bedrock 0.5 m +
Shell and auger, 6 in (152 mm) diameter
July 1972

LOG

Geological classification	Lithology	Thickness m	Depth m
	Soil; brown	0.1	0.1
River Terrace Deposit (Eighth Terrace)	Clay, sandy, with angular to subrounded and rounded flint, and rounded white quartz; yellowish brown	0.4	0.5
Clay-with-flints	Clay, black mottling, reddish brown, with fine to cobble-size flints and rare rounded white quartz	2.1	2.6
Upper Chalk	Chalk, soft; white	0.5+	3.1

Surface level (+170.1 m) +558 ft
Water not struck
Shell and auger, 6 in (152 mm) diameter
July 1972

Overburden 1.3 m
Mineral 6.1 m
Bedrock 0.5 m +

LOG

Geological classification	Lithology	Thickness m	Depth m
Made ground	Clay, brown	0.6	0.6
	Clay, silty, with occasional fine flint pebbles; dark brown	0.7	1.3

Sand and gravel of unknown origin	'Clayey gravel, with the base of the deposit (6.3 m–7.4 m) being very clayey with cobbles of flint
	    Gravel: fine to coarse with cobbles, subangular to subrounded grey and white coated (patina) flint, rounded white quartz and rounded reddish brown quartzite, occasional brownish black ironstone
	    Sand: medium with fine and coarse, clayey throughout, black (manganese ?) staining near the base; orange-brown
		6.1	7.4

Upper Chalk	Chalk, soft, with coarse to cobble-size nodular flints; white	0.5+	7.9

GRADING

Mean for deposit *percentages*			Depth below surface (m)	*percentages*						
Fines	Sand	Gravel		Fines	Sand				Gravel	
				$-\frac{1}{16}$	$+\frac{1}{16}-\frac{1}{4}$	$+\frac{1}{4}-1$	$+1-4$	$+4-16$	$+16-64$	$+64$
19	15	66	1.3–2.3	16	0	10	14	6	54	0
			2.3–3.3	7	0	9	1	5	78	0
			3.3–4.3	10	1	6	3	11	69	0
			4.3–5.3	19	2	15	3	12	49	0
			5.3–6.3	21	1	14	7	27	30	0
			6.3–7.4	37	0	2	2	7	52	0
			Mean	19	1	9	5	11	55	0

COMPOSITION

Depth below surface (m)	Percentages (in +4−16 mm fraction)					
	Flint	Quartz and quartzite	Limestone	Chalk	Ironstone	Minor constituents
1.3–2.3	43	57	—	—	—	—
2.3–3.3	68	32	—	—	—	—
3.3–4.3	57	36	—	—	5	2
4.3–5.3	45	52	—	—	1	2
5.3–6.3	45	52	—	—	3	—
6.3–7.4	94	6	—	—	—	—
Mean	52	45	—	—	2	1

SU 68 SE 7   6523 8180   Exlade Street, Woodcote

Surface level (+171.9 m) +564 ft   Waste 0.3 m
Water not struck   Bedrock 1.8 m+
Shell and auger, 6 in (152 mm) diameter
July 1972

LOG

Geological classification	Lithology	Thickness m	Depth m
	Soil	0.3	0.3
Reading Beds	Clay, silty and sandy with occasional flint pebbles; dark brown	1.3	1.6
Upper Chalk	Chalk, soft with occasional brown clay seams; cream-white	0.5+	2.1

SU 68 SE 8   6683 8083   Whitewood Heath, Checkendon   **Block D**

Surface level (+121.9 m) +400 ft   Waste 5.3 m
Water not struck   Bedrock 0.5 m+
Shell and auger, 6 in (152 mm) diameter
January 1972

LOG

Geological classification	Lithology	Thickness m	Depth m
	Soil, brown	0.2	0.2
River Terrace Deposits (Seventh−Eighth Terrace)	Clay, silty and sandy, with occasional flint and quartzite pebbles, mottled brown; orange-brown	1.6	1.8
Clay-with-flints	Clay, dark brown, with fine to cobble-size, angular to subrounded flints, some brownish black (manganese ?) staining throughout	3.5	5.3
Upper Chalk	Chalk, soft, with flints; white	0.5+	5.8

Surface level (+119.5 m) +392 ft
Water not struck
Shell and auger, 6 in (152 mm) diameter
January 1972

Overburden 1.1 m
Mineral 4.7 m
Bedrock 0.5 m +

LOG

Geological classification	Lithology	Thickness m	Depth m
	Soil; brown	0.2	0.2
River Terrace Deposits (Seventh–Eighth Terrace)	Clay, silty and sandy, with fine to medium, angular to subangular flint, and occasional rounded quartzite; brown to orange-brown	0.9	1.1
	'Very clayey' gravel, with the base of the deposit (4.6 m–5.8 m) consisting of nodular flint cobbles in a brown clay matrix (Clay-with-flints?)	4.7	5.8
	Gravel: fine to coarse with cobbles, mainly subangular to subrounded flint with rounded quartz and quartzite, occasional chalk and brown ironstone with rare green siltstone		
	Sand: medium with coarse and fine, mainly quartz with flint, clayey throughout; brown		
Upper Chalk	Chalk, soft, with flints; white	0.5+	6.3

GRADING

Mean for deposit *percentages*			Depth below surface (m)	*percentages*						
Fines	Sand	Gravel		Fines	Sand			Gravel		
				$-\frac{1}{16}$	$+\frac{1}{16}-\frac{1}{4}$	$+\frac{1}{4}-1$	$+1-4$	$+4-16$	$+16-64$	$+64$
24	32	44	1.1–5.8	24	6	16	10	16	28	0

COMPOSITION

Depth below surface (m)	Percentages (in +4−16 mm fraction)				
	Flint	Quartz and quartzite	Chalk	Ironstone	Minor constituents
1.1–5.8	60	26	10	3	1

Surface level (+119.5 m) +392 ft

Water not struck

Shell and auger, 6 in (152 mm) diameter

September 1972

Overburden 4.0 m

Mineral 3.3 m

Bedrock 0.5 m +

LOG

Geological classification	Lithology	Thickness m	Depth m
	Soil; brown	0.1	0.1
River Terrace Deposits (Sixth-Seventh Terrace)	Clay, sandy, with fine to coarse pebbles of angular to rounded grey and white coated (patina) flint, rounded white quartz, well rounded black and light brown quartzite with occasional ironstone and chalk; brown becoming reddish brown	3.9	4.0
	'Very clayey' gravel;	3.3	7.3
	Gravel: fine to coarse with occasional cobbles, angular to subrounded, grey and white coated (patina) flint, well rounded white quartz, well rounded white to brown quartzite, occasional chalk, brownish black ironstone and assortment of sandstone, metamorphic and igneous fragments		
	Sand: medium with some coarse and fine, mainly quartz with flint, clayey throughout; light brown		
Upper Chalk	Chalk, soft; white	0.5+	7.8

GRADING

Mean for deposit percentages			Depth below surface (m)	percentages							
Fines	Sand	Gravel		Fines	Sand				Gravel		
				$-\frac{1}{16}$	$+\frac{1}{16}-\frac{1}{4}$	$+\frac{1}{4}-1$	$+1-4$		$+4-16$	$+16-64$	$+64$
25	24	51	4.0–5.0	28	2	12	6		14	38	0
			5.0–6.0	19	2	23	4		22	30	0
			6.0–7.3	27	2	17	6		17	31	0
			Mean	25	2	17	5		18	33	0

COMPOSITION

Depth below surface (m)	Percentages (in +4−16 mm fraction)				
	Flint	Quartz and quartzite	Chalk	Ironstone	Minor constituents
4.0–5.0	41	51	—	8	—
5.0–6.0	56	30	—	4	10
6.0–7.3	41	45	—	3	11
Mean	46	41	tr	6	7

Surface level (+ 103.9 m) + 341 ft
Water not struck
Shell and auger, 6 in (152 mm) diameter
January 1972

Overburden 0.4 m
Mineral 7.0 m
Bedrock 0.6 m +

LOG

Geological classification	Lithology	Thickness m	Depth m
	Soil; sandy and pebbly clay; orange-brown	0.4	0.4
River Terrace Deposits (Sixth–Seventh Terrace)	'Very clayey' sandy gravel with base of the deposit (5.5 m–7.4 m) consisting of nodular flint cobbles in a dark brown clay matrix (Clay-with-flints?)	7.0	7.4
	Gravel: fine to coarse with cobbles, mainly angular to subangular flint with well rounded quartz and quartzite, occasional chalk (at base of deposit) and brownish black ironstone		
	Sand: dominantly medium, with occasional fine and coarse, quartz with flint, clayey in parts; orange-brown to dark brown		
Upper Chalk	Chalk, soft, with flint; white	0.6+	8.0

GRADING

Mean for deposit *percentages*			Depth below surface (m)	*percentages*						
Fines	Sand	Gravel		Fines	Sand			Gravel		
				$-\frac{1}{16}$	$+\frac{1}{16}-\frac{1}{4}$	$+\frac{1}{4}-1$	$+1-4$	$+4-16$	$+16-64$	$+64$
22	42	36	0.4–1.5	25	1	26	14	24	10	0
			1.5–2.5	25	5	17	8	19	26	0
			2.5–3.5	21	5	48	5	10	11	0
			3.5–4.5	15	10	54	3	8	10	0
			4.5–5.5	10	8	45	3	11	23	0
			5.5–7.4	31	5	10	3	9	42	0
			Mean	22	6	30	6	13	23	0

COMPOSITION

Depth below surface (m)	Percentages (in +4−16 mm fraction)				
	Flint	Quartz and quartzite	Chalk	Ironstone	Minor constituents
0.4–1.5	44	40	—	9	7
1.5–2.5	27	58	—	15	—
2.5–3.5	28	62	—	10	—
3.5–4.5	47	42	—	7	4
4.5–5.5	67	33	—	—	—
5.5–7.4	57	7	24	12	—
Mean	47	27	13	12	1

Surface level (c + 131.1 m) c + 430 ft
Water not struck
Shell and auger, 8 in (203 mm) diameter
September 1975

Mineral 2.0 m
Waste 3.9 m
Bedrock 0.2 m +

LOG

Geological classification	Lithology	Thickness m	Depth m

River Terrace Deposits (Sixth–Eighth Terrace	'Very clayey' gravel
	    Gravel: fine to coarse with occasional cobbles, mainly well rounded white quartz, well rounded brown and reddish brown quartzite with angular to subangular black and white coated (patina) flint; occasional blackish brown ironstone
	    Sand: fine to coarse, mainly quartz with flint, clayey throughout; reddish brown
		2.0	2.0

Clay-with-flints	Clay, reddish brown with black (manganese ?) streaks; coarse to cobble-size, angular to subrounded, nodular black and white coated (patina) flints, with occasional well rounded quartz and quartzite, rare ironstone	3.0	5.0
	Clay, with rare flint, occasional black (manganese ?) streaks; dark brown	0.9	5.9
Upper Chalk	Chalk, soft; white	0.2+	6.1

GRADING

Mean for deposit percentages			Depth below surface (m)	percentages						
Fines	Sand	Gravel		Fines	Sand			Gravel		
				$-\frac{1}{16}$	$+\frac{1}{16}-\frac{1}{4}$	$+\frac{1}{4}-1$	$+1-4$	$+4-16$	$+16-64$	$+64$
27	24	49	0.0–1.0	17	6	6	9	21	35	6
			1.0–2.0	36	9	10	7	17	21	0
			Mean	27	8	8	8	19	27	3

COMPOSITION

Depth below surface (m)	Percentages (in +4−16 mm fraction)				
	Flint	Quartz and quartzite	Limestone and chalk	Ironstone	Minor constituents
0.0–1.0	35	60	—	5	—
1.0–2.0	41	53	—	6	—
Mean	38	56	—	6	tr
	Percentages (in +16 mm fraction)				
0–1	76	22	—	—	2
1–2	48	51	—	—	1
Mean	62	37	—	—	1

Surface level (+136.6 m) +448 ft
Water not struck
Trench section
July 1975

Overburden 0.1 m
Mineral 3.5 m
Bedrock 0.1 m +

LOG

Geological classification	Lithology	Thickness m	Depth m
	Soil; greyish brown	0.1	0.1

Sand and gravel of unknown origin	'Clayey' gravel
	    Gravel: fine to coarse with occasional cobbles, mainly angular to well rounded grey and brown flint with well-rounded white quartz and occasional well rounded quartzite, ironstone and chalk pellets
	    Sand: fine to coarse, mainly quartz with flint, silty in parts, occasional black (manganese ?) staining; orange-brown to brown
		3.5	3.6

Upper Chalk	Chalk, soft; white	0.1+	3.7

GRADING

Mean for deposit *percentages*			Depth below surface (m)	*percentages*						
Fines	Sand	Gravel		Fines	Sand			Gravel		
				$-\frac{1}{16}$	$+\frac{1}{16}-\frac{1}{4}$	$+\frac{1}{4}-1$	$+1-4$	$+4-16$	$+16-64$	$+64$
13	31	56	0.1–3.6	13	12	10	9	32	21	3

COMPOSITION

Depth below surface (m)	Percentages (in +4−16 mm fraction)				
	Flint	Quartz and quartzite	Chalk	Ironstone	Minor constituents
0.1–3.6	62	32	1	3	2
	Percentages (in +16 mm fraction)				
0.1–3.6	92	2	1	—	5

APPENDIX G

LIST OF WORKINGS

By the end of 1976 there was one large active working pit situated north of the A423 near Oakley Wood (642 887) in the Wallingford Fan Gravels.

In the resource sheet area the total worked out area is 0.36 km². Brief details of workings indicating their known extent up to 1976 are given in Table 9. Many of the disused workings have been or are being filled.

WORKINGS AT TIME OF SURVEY

Location	Drift deposit	Grid reference	Approximate area (km 2)
A *Working pit* North of A423 Oakley Wood: Benson	Wallingford Fan Gravels	642 887	0.02
B *Disused pits* North of A423 Oakley Wood: Benson	Wallingford Fan Gravels	642 890	0.19
South of A423 Oakley Wood: Crowmarsh	Wallingford Fan Gravels	641 885	0.06
South of A423 Blenheim Farm: Crowmarsh	Wallingford Fan Gravels	638 883	0.02
South of A423 Foxberry Woods: Crowmarsh	Wallingford Fan Gravels	643 880	0.02
Near Fair Mile Hospital: Cholsey	Second Terrace of River Thames	595 860	0.05
Total area			0.36

APPENDIX H:

CONVERSION TABLE, METRES TO FEET (to nearest 0.5 ft)

m	ft	m	ft	m	ft	m	ft	m	ft
0.1	0.5	6.1	20	12.1	39.5	18.1	59.5	24.1	79
0.2	0.5	6.2	20.5	12.2	40	18.2	59.5	24.2	79.5
0.3	1	6.3	20.5	12.3	40.5	18.3	60	24.3	79.5
0.4	1.5	6.4	21	12.4	40.5	18.4	60.5	24.4	80
0.5	1.5	6.5	21.5	12.5	41	18.5	60.5	24.5	80.5
0.6	2	6.6	21.5	12.6	41.5	18.6	61	24.6	80.5
0.7	2.5	6.7	22	12.7	41.5	18.7	61.5	24.7	81
0.8	2.5	6.8	22.5	12.8	42	18.8	61.5	24.8	81.5
0.9	3	6.9	22.5	12.9	42.5	18.9	62	24.9	81.5
1.0	3.5	7.0	23	13.0	42.5	19.0	62.5	25.0	82
1.1	3.5	7.1	23.5	13.1	43	19.1	62.5	25.1	82.5
1.2	4	7.2	23.5	13.2	43.5	19.2	63	25.2	82.5
1.3	4.5	7.3	24	13.3	43.5	19.3	63.5	25.3	83
1.4	4.5	7.4	24.5	13.4	44	19.4	63.5	25.4	83.5
1.5	5	7.5	24.5	13.5	44.5	19.5	64	25.5	83.5
1.6	5	7.6	25	13.6	44.5	19.6	64.5	25.6	84
1.7	5.5	7.7	25.5	13.7	45	19.7	64.5	25.7	84.5
1.8	6	7.8	25.5	13.8	45.5	19.8	65	25.8	84.5
1.9	6	7.9	26	13.9	45.5	19.9	65.5	25.9	85
2.0	6.5	8.0	26	14.0	46	20.0	65.5	26.0	85.5
2.1	7	8.1	26.5	14.1	46.5	20.1	66	26.1	85.5
2.2	7	8.2	27	14.2	46.5	20.2	66.5	26.2	86
2.3	7.5	8.3	27	14.3	47	20.3	66.5	26.3	86.5
2.4	8	8.4	27.5	14.4	47	20.4	67	26.4	86.5
2.5	8	8.5	28	14.5	47.5	20.5	67.5	26.5	87
2.6	8.5	8.6	28	14.6	48	20.6	67.5	26.6	87.5
2.7	9	8.7	28.5	14.7	48	20.7	68	26.7	87.5
2.8	9	8.8	29	14.8	48.5	20.8	68	26.8	88
2.9	9.5	8.9	29	14.9	49	20.9	68.5	26.9	88.5
3.0	10	9.0	29.5	15.0	49	21.0	69	27.0	88.5
3.1	10	9.1	30	15.1	49.5	21.1	69	27.1	89
3.2	10.5	9.2	30	15.2	50.0	21.2	69.5	27.2	89
3.3	11	9.3	30.5	15.3	50	21.3	70	27.3	89.5
3.4	11	9.4	31	15.4	50.5	21.4	70	27.4	90
3.5	11.5	9.5	31	15.5	51	21.5	70.5	27.5	90
3.6	12	9.6	31.5	15.6	51	21.6	71	27.6	90.5
3.7	12	9.7	32	15.7	51.5	21.7	71	27.7	91
3.8	12.5	9.8	32	15.8	52	21.8	71.5	27.8	91
3.9	13	9.9	32.5	15.9	52	21.9	72	27.9	91.5
4.0	13	10.0	33	16.0	52.5	22.0	72	28.0	92
4.1	13.5	10.1	33	16.1	53	22.1	72.5	28.1	92
4.2	14	10.2	33.5	16.2	53	22.2	73	28.2	92.5
4.3	14	10.3	34	16.3	53.5	22.3	73	28.3	93
4.4	14.5	10.4	34	16.4	54	22.4	73.5	28.4	93
4.5	15	10.5	34.5	16.5	54	22.5	74	28.5	93.5
4.6	15	10.6	35	16.6	54.5	22.6	74	28.6	94
4.7	15.5	10.7	35	16.7	55	22.7	74.5	28.7	94
4.8	15.5	10.8	35.5	16.8	55	22.8	75	28.8	94.5
4.9	16	10.9	36	16.9	55.5	22.9	75	28.9	95
5.0	16.5	11.0	36	17.0	56	23.0	75.5	29.0	95
5.1	17	11.1	36.5	17.1	56	23.1	76	29.1	95.5
5.2	17	11.2	36.5	17.2	56.5	23.2	76	29.2	96
5.3	17.5	11.3	37	17.3	57	23.3	76.5	29.3	96
5.4	17.5	11.4	37.5	17.4	57	23.4	77	29.4	96.5
5.5	18	11.5	37.5	17.5	57.5	23.5	77	29.5	97
5.6	18.5	11.6	38	17.6	57.5	23.6	77.5	29.6	97
5.7	18.5	11.7	38.5	17.7	58	23.7	78	29.7	97.5
5.8	19	11.8	38.5	17.8	58.5	23.8	78	29.8	98
5.9	19.5	11.9	39	17.9	58.5	23.9	78.5	29.9	98
6.0	19.5	12.0	39.5	18.0	59	24.0	78.5	30.0	98.5

REFERENCES

ALLEN, V. T. 1936. Terminology of medium-grained sediments. *Rep. Natl Res. Counc. Washington, 1935–36, App. 1, Rep. Comm. Sedimentation*, pp. 18–47.

ARCHER, A. A. 1969. Background and problems of an assessment of sand and gravel resources in the United Kingdom. *Proc. 9th Commonw. Min. Metall. Congr., 1969.* Vol. 2, Mining and petroleum geology, pp. 495–508. (London: Institution of Mining and Metallurgy).

— 1970a. Standardisation of the size classification of naturally occurring particles. *Géotechnique*, Vol. 20, pp. 103–107.

— 1970(b). Making the most of metrication. *Quarry Managers' J.*, Vol. 54, pp. 223–227.

ARKELL, W. J. 1947 The geology of Oxford. (Oxford: Clarendon Press).

ATTERBERG, A. 1905. Die rationelle Klassifikation der Sande und Kiese. *Chem. Ztg.*, Vol. 29, pp. 195–198.

BRITISH STANDARD 1377. 1967. *Methods of testing soils for civil engineering purposes*. (London: British Standards Institution.)

BUREAU OF MINES AND GEOLOGICAL SURVEY. 1948. *Mineral resources of the United States*. (Washington DC: Public Affairs Press.) pp. 14–17.

JUKES-BROWN, A. J. AND OSBORNE WHITE, H. J. 1908. The geology of the country around Henley-on-Thames. *Mem. Geol. Surv. GB.*

HARRIS, P. M., THURRELL, R. G., HEALING, R. A. and ARCHER, A. A. 1974. Aggregates in Britain. *Proc. R. Soc. London*, Ser. A, Vol. 339, pp. 329–353.

HEY, R. W. 1965. Highly Quartzose Pebble Gravels in the London Basin. *Proc. Geol. Assoc.*, 76, pp. 403–420.

LANE, E. W. and others. 1974. Report of the sub-committee on sediment terminology. *Trans. Am. Geophys. Union*, Vol. 28, pp. 936–938.

PETTIJOHN, F. J. 1957. *Sedimentary rocks*, 2nd Ed. (London: Harper and Row.)

SANDFORD, K. S. 1924. The river gravels of the Oxford District. *Q.J. Geol. Soc. London*, Vol. 80, pp. 113–170.

— 1926. in POCOCK, T. I. The geology of the country around Oxford. *Mem. Geol. Surv. GB.*, pp. 104–172.

THURRELL, R. G. 1971. The assessment of mineral resources with particular reference to sand and gravel. *Quarry Managers' J.*, Vol. 55, pp. 19–25.

TWENHOFEL, W. H. 1937. Terminology of the fine-grained mechanical sediments. *Rep. Natl Res. Counc. Washington, 1936–7, App. 1, Rep. Comm. Sedimentation*, pp. 81–104.

UDDEN, J. A. 1914. Mechanical composition of clastic sediments. *Bull. Geol. Soc. Am.*, Vol. 25, pp. 655–744.

WENTWORTH, C. K. 1922. A scale of grade and class terms for clastic sediments. *J. Geol.*, Vol. 30, No. 5, pp. 377–392.

— 1935. The terminology of coarse sediments. *Bull. Natl Res. Counc. Washington*, No. 98, pp. 225–246.

WILLMAN, H. B. 1942. Geology and mineral resources of the Marseilles, Ottawa and Streator quadrangles. *Bull. Illinois State Geol. Surv.*, No. 66, pp. 343–344.

WOOLDRIDGE, S. W. 1938. The Glaciation of the London Basin and the Evolution of the Lower Thames Drainage System. *Q. J. Geol. Soc. London*, Vol. 94, pp. 627–667.

The following reports of the Institute relate particularly to bulk mineral resources

Reports of the Institute of Geological Sciences

Assessment of British Sand and Gravel Resources

1   The sand and gravel resources of the country south-east of Norwich, Norfolk: Resource sheet TG 20.   E. F. P. Nickless.
Report 71/20   ISBN 0 11 880216 X   £1.15

2   The sand and gravel resources of the country around Witham, Essex: Resource sheet TL 81.   H. J. E. Haggard.
Report 72/6   ISBN 0 11 880588 6   £1.20

3   The sand and gravel resources of the area south and west of Woodbridge, Suffolk: Resource sheet TM 24.   R. Allender and S. E. Hollyer.
Report 72/9   ISBN 0 11 880596 7   £1.70

4   The sand and gravel resources of the country around Maldon, Essex: Resource sheet TL 80.   J. D. Ambrose.
Report 73/1   ISBN 0 11 880600 9   £1.20

5   The sand and gravel resources of the country around Hethersett, Norfolk: Resource sheet TG 10.   E. F. P. Nickless.
Report 73/4   ISBN 0 11 880606 8   £1.60

6   The sand and gravel resources of the country around Terling, Essex: Resource sheet TL 71.   C. H. Eaton.
Report 73/5   ISBN 0 11 880608 4   £1.20

7   The sand and gravel resources of the country around Layer Breton and Tolleshunt D'Arcy, Essex: Resource sheet TL 91 and part of TL 90.   J. D. Ambrose.
Report 73/8   ISBN 0 11 880614 9   £1.30

8   The sand and gravel resources of the country around Shotley and Felixstowe, Suffolk: Resource sheet TM 23.   R. Allender and S. E. Hollyer.
Report 73/13   ISBN 0 11 880625 4   £1.60

9   The sand and gravel resources of the country around Attlebridge, Norfolk: Resource sheet TG 11.   E. F. P. Nickless.
Report 73/15   ISBN 0 11 880658 0   £1.85

10   The sand and gravel resources of the country west of Colchester, Essex: Resource sheet TL 92.   J. D. Ambrose.
Report 74/6   ISBN 0 11 880671 8   £1.45

11   The sand and gravel resources of the country around Tattingstone, Suffolk: Resource sheet TM 13.   S. E. Hollyer.
Report 74/9   ISBN 0 11 880675 0   £1.95

12   The sand and gravel resources of the country around Gerrards Cross, Buckinghamshire: Resource sheet SU 99, TQ 08 and TQ 09.   H. C. Squirrell.
Report 74/14   ISBN 0 11 880710 2   £2.20

Mineral Assessment Reports

13   The sand and gravel resources of the country east of Chelmsford, Essex: Resource sheet TL 70.   M. R. Clarke.
ISBN 0 11 880744 7   £3.50

14   The sand and gravel resources of the country east of Colchester, Essex: Resource sheet TM 02.   J. D. Ambrose.
ISBN 0 11 880745 5   £3.25

15   The sand and gravel resources of the country around Newton on Trent, Lincolnshire: Resource sheet SK 87.   D. Price.
ISBN 0 11 880746 3   £3.00

16   The sand and gravel resources of the country around Braintree, Essex: Resource sheet TL 72.   M. R. Clarke.
ISBN 0 11 880747 1   £3.50

17   The sand and gravel resources of the country around Besthorpe, Nottinghamshire: Resource sheet SK 86 and part of SK 76.   J. R. Gozzard.
ISBN 0 11 880748 X   £3.00

18   The sand and gravel resources of the Thames Valley, the country around Cricklade, Wiltshire: Resource sheet SU 09/19 and parts of SP 00/10.   P. R. Robson.
ISBN 0 11 880749 8   £3.00

19   The sand and gravel resources of the country south of Gainsborough, Lincolnshire: Resource sheet SK 88 and part of SK 78.   J. H. Lovell.
ISBN 0 11 880750 1   £2.50

20   The sand and gravel resources of the country east of Newark upon Trent, Nottinghamshire: Resource sheet SK 85.   J. R. Gozzard.
ISBN 0 11 880751 X   £2.75

21   The sand and gravel resources of the Thames and Kennet Valleys, the country around Pangbourne, Berkshire: Resource sheet SU 67.   H. C. Squirrell.
ISBN 0 11 880752 8   £3.25

22   The sand and gravel resources of the country north-west of Scunthorpe, Humberside: Resource sheet SE 81.   J. W. C. James.
ISBN 0 11 880753 6   £3.00

23   The sand and gravel resources of the Thames Valley, the country between Lechlade and Standlake: Resource sheet SP 30 and parts of SP 20, SU 29 and SU 39.   P. Robson.
ISBN 0 11 881252 1   £7.25

24   The sand and gravel resources of the country around Aldermaston, Berkshire: Resource sheet SU 56 and SU 66.   H. C. Squirrell.
ISBN 0 11 881253 X   £5.00

25   The celestite resources of the area north-east of Bristol: Resource sheet ST 68 and parts of ST 59, 69, 79, 58, 78, 68 and 77.   E. F. P. Nickless, S. J. Booth and P. N. Mosley.
ISBN 0 11 881262 9   £5.00

26   The limestone and dolomite resources of the country around Monyash, Derbyshire: Resource sheet SK 16.   F. C. Cox and D. McC. Bridge.
ISBN 0 11 881263 7   £7.00

27   The sand and gravel resources of the country west and south of Lincoln, Lincolnshire: Resource sheets SK 95, SK 96 and SK 97.   I. Jackson.
ISBN 0 11 884003 7   £6.00

28   The sand and gravel resources of the country around Eynsham, Oxfordshire: Resource sheet SP 40 and part of SP 41.   W. J. R. Harries.
ISBN 0 11 884012 6   £3.00

29   The sand and gravel resources of the country south-west of Scunthorpe, Humberside: Resource sheet SE 80.   J. H. Lovell.
ISBN 0 11 884013 4   £3.50

30   Procedure for the assessment of limestone resources.   F. C. Cox, D. McC. Bridge and J. H. Hull.
ISBN 0 11 884030 4   £1.25

31   The sand and gravel resources of the country west of Newark upon Trent, Nottinghamshire: Resource sheet SK 75.   D. Price and P. J. Rogers.
ISBN 0 11 884031 2   £3.50

32   The sand and gravel resources of the country around Sonning and Henley, Berkshire, Oxfordshire and Buckinghamshire: Resource sheet SU 77 and SU 78.   H. C. Squirrell.
ISBN 0 11 884032 0   £5.25

33   The sand and gravel resources of the country north of Gainsborough, Lincolnshire: Resource sheet SK 89.   J. R. Gozzard and D. Price
ISBN 0 11 884033 9   £4.50

34   The sand and gravel resources of the Dengie Peninsula, Essex: Resource sheet TL 90, etc.   M. B. Simmons.
ISBN 0 11 884081 9   £5.00

35   The sand and gravel resources of the country around Darvel, Strathclyde: Resource sheet NS 53, 63, etc.   E. F. P. Nickless, A. M. Aitken and A. A. McMillan.
ISBN 0 11 884082 7   £7.00

36   The sand and gravel resources of the country around Southend-on-Sea, Essex: Resource sheets TQ 78/79 etc. S. E. Hollyer and M. B. Simmons.
ISBN 0 11 884083 5   £7.50

37   The sand and gravel resources of the country around Bawtrey, South Yorkshire: Resource sheet SK 69.   A. R. Clayton.
ISBN 0 11 884053 3   £5.75

38   The sand and gravel resources of the country around Abingdon, Oxfordshire: Resource sheet SU 49, 59, SP 40, 50. C. E. Corser.
ISBN 0 11 884084 5   £5.50

39   The sand and gravel resources of the Blackwater Valley (Aldershot) area: Resource sheet SU 85, 86, parts SU 84, 94, 95, 96.   M. R. Clarke, A. J. Dixon and M. Kubala.
ISBN 0 11 884085 1   £7.00

40   The sand and gravel resources of the country west of Darlington, County Durham: Resource sheet NZ 11, 21. A. Smith.
ISBN 0 11 884086 X   £4.75

41   The sand and gravel resources of the country around Garmouth, Grampian Region: Resource sheet NJ 36.   A. M. Aitken, J. W. Merritt and A. J. Shaw.
ISBN 0 11 884090 8   £8.75

42   The sand and gravel resources of the country around Maidenhead and Marlow: Resource sheet SU 88, parts SU 87, 97, 98.   P. N. Dunkley.
ISBN 0 11 884091 6   £5.00

43   The sand and gravel resources of the country around Misterton, Nottinghamshire: Resource sheet SK 79. D. Thomas and D. Price
ISBN 0 11 884092 4   £5.25

44   The sand and gravel resources of the country around Sedgefield, Durham: Resource sheet NZ 32.   M. D. A. Samuel.
ISBN 0 11 884093 2   £5.75

45   The sand and gravel resources of the country around Brampton, Cumbria: Resource sheet NY 55, part 56. I. Jackson.
ISBN 0 11 884094 0   £6.75

46   The sand and gravel resources of the country around Harlow, Essex: Resource sheet TL 41.   P. M. Hopson.
ISBN 0 11 884107 6   £9.50

47   The limestone and dolomite resources of the country around Wirksworth, Derbyshire: Resource sheet SK 25, part 35.   F. C. Cox and D. J. Harrison.
ISBN 0 11 884108 4   £15.00

48   The sand and gravel resources of the Loddon Valley area: Sheets SU 75, 76, parts 64, 65, 66 and 74.   M. R. Clarke, E. J. Raynor and R. A. Sobey.
ISBN 0 11 884109 2   £8.75

49   The sand and gravel resources of the country around Lanark, Strathclyde Region: Resource sheet NS 94, part 84. J. L. Laxton and E. F. P. Nickless.
ISBN 0 11 884112 2   £11.00

50   The sand and gravel resources of the country around Fordingbridge, Hampshire: Resource sheet SU 11 and parts of SU 00, 01, 10, 20 and 21.   M. Kubala.
ISBN 0 11 884111 4   £7.75

51   The sand and gravel resources of the country north of Bournemouth, Dorset: Resource sheet SU 00, 10, 20, SZ 09, 19 and 29.   M. R. Clarke.
ISBN 0 11 884112 2   £9.75

52   The sand and gravel resources of the country between Hatfield Heath and Great Waltham, Essex: Resource sheet TL 51 and 61.   R. J. Marks.
ISBN 0 11 884113 0   £8.00

53   The sand and gravel resources of the country around Cottenham, Cambridgeshire: Resource sheet TL 46 and 47. A. J. Dixon.
ISBN 0 11 884114 9   £9.25

54   The sand and gravel resources of the country around Huntingdon and St Ives, Cambridgeshire: Resource sheets TL 16, 17, 26, 27, 36 and 37.   R. W. Gatliff.
ISBN 0 11 884115 7   £8.75

55   The sand and gravel resources of the country around Ipswich, Suffolk: Resource sheet TM 14.   R. Allender and S. E. Hollyer.
ISBN 0 11 884116 5   £10.00

56   Procedure for the assessment of the conglomerate resources of the Sherwood Sandstone Group. D. P. Piper and P. J. Rogers.
ISBN 0 11 884143 2   £1.25

57   The conglomerate resources of the Sherwood Sandstone Group of the country around Cheadle, Staffordshire: Resource Sheet SK 04. P. J. Rogers, D. P. Piper and T. J. Charsley.
ISBN 0 11 884144 0   £7.75

58   The sand and gravel resources of the country west of Peterhead, Grampian Region: Resource sheet NK 04, and parts of NJ 94 and 95, NK 05, 14 and 15. A. A. McMillan and A. M. Aitken.
ISBN 0 11 884145 9   £12.00

59   The sand and gravel resources of the country around Newbury, Berkshire: Resource sheets SU 46 and 57, parts of SU 36, 37 and 47. J. R. Gozzard.
ISBN 0 11 884146 7   £11.00

60   The sand and gravel resources of the country south-west of Peterborough, in Cambridgeshire and east Northamptonshire: Resource sheets TL 09 and 19, and SP 98 and TL 08. A. M. Harrisson.
ISBN 0 11 884147 5   £15.50

61   The sand and gravel resources of the country north of Wrexham, Clwyd: Resource sheet SJ 35 and part of SJ 25. P. N. Dunkley.
ISBN 0 11 884148 3   £11.75

62   The sand and gravel resources of the country around Dolphinton, Strathclyde Region, and West Linton, Borders Region: Resource Sheets NT 04 and 14, and parts of NT 05 and 15. A. A. McMillan, J. L. Laxton and A. J. Shaw.
ISBN 0 11 884149 1   £8.00

63   The sand and gravel resources of the valley of the Douglas Water, Strathclyde: Resource sheet NS 83 and parts of NS 82, 92 and 93. A. J. Shaw and E. F. P. Nickless.
ISBN 0 11 884150 5   £11.50

64   The sand and gravel resources of the country between Wallingford and Goring, Oxfordshire: Resource sheet SU 68 and part SU 58. C. E. Corser.
ISBN 0 11 884151 3   £11.50

Reports of the Institute of Geological Sciences

Other Reports

69/9   Sand and gravel resources of the inner Moray Firth. A. L. Harris and J. D. Peacock.
ISBN 0 11 880106 6   35p

70/4   Sands and gravels of the southern counties of Scotland. G. A. Goodlet.
ISBN 0 11 880105 8   90p

72/8   The use and resources of moulding sand in Northern Ireland.   R. A. Old.
ISBN 0 11 881594 0   30p

73/9   The superficial deposits of the Firth of Clyde and its sea lochs.   C. E. Deegan, R. Kirby, I. Rae and R. Floyd.
ISBN 0 11 880617 3   95p

77/1   Sources of aggregate in Northern Ireland (2nd edition).   I. B. Cameron.
ISBN 0 11 881279 3   70p

77/2   Sand and gravel resources of the Grampian Region.   J. D. Peacock and others.
ISBN 0 11 881282 3   80p

77/5   Sand and gravel resources of the Fife Region.   M. A. E. Browne.
ISBN 0 11 884004 5   60p

77/6   Sand and gravel resources of the Tayside Region.   I. B. Paterson.
ISBN 0 11 884008 8   £1.40

77/8   Sand and gravel resources of the Strathclyde Region.   I. B. Cameron and others.
ISBN 0 11 884028 2   £2.50

77/9   Sand and gravel resources of the Central Region, Scotland.   M. A. E. Browne.
ISBN 0 11 884016 9   £1.35

77/19   Sand and gravel resources of the Borders Region, Scotland.   A. D. McAdam.
ISBN 0 11 884025 8   £1.00

77/22   Sand and gravel resources of the Dumfries and Galloway Region of Scotland.   I. B. Cameron.
ISBN 0 11 884021 5   £1.20

78/1   Sand and gravels of the Lothian Region of Scotland.   A. D. McAdam.
ISBN 0 11 884042 8   £1.00

78/8   Sand and gravel resources of the Highland Region.   W. Mykura, D. L. Ross and F. May.
ISBN 0 11 884050 9   £3.00

Dd 696491   K8

Typeset for the Institute of Geological Sciences by Trendsetter Photoset Limited, Brentwood, Essex.

Printed in England for Her Majesty's Stationery Office by Commercial Colour Press, London E7.